The Dreamcatcher Trilogy · Volume One

The Transparent Eyeball

SHARON KAYE

Royal Fireworks Press
Unionville, New York

Royal Fireworks Press
P.O. Box 399
41 First Avenue
Unionville, NY 10988-0399
(845) 726-4444
fax: (845) 726-3824
email: mail@rfwp.com
website: rfwp.com

ISBN: 978-0-88092-951-6

Publisher: Dr. T.M. Kemnitz
Editor: Jennifer Ault
Book and Cover Designer: Kerri Ann Ruhl

Printed and bound in Unionville, New York, on acid-free paper
using vegetable-based inks at the Royal Fireworks facility. 28ap20

local 363

Our truest life is when we are in dreams awake.

— Henry David Thoreau

"Transparent Eyeball" by Christopher Pearse Cranch, ca. 1836-1838

CHAPTER ONE

I'm out of sync. That's the only way to explain it.

It's like I'm listening to one soundtrack, and everybody else is listening to another one. I zig; they zag. I zag; they zig. There's a lot of them and just one of me. That makes it look like I'm wrong—all wrong.

Take my post to the neighborhood social media page the other night. One of my neighbors posted that she "heard a loud, crashing noise coming from the pond." And so I posted, "I dare everyone to go to sleep tonight."

I thought it was funny. It was supposed to be a joke. From my point of view, it was—and still is—a joke. Not a threat. A harmless joke.

Anyhow, stuff they think is funny I don't find funny at all. There was the thing in the courtyard at school. I did it because she was laughing at me. I feel like she and her friends are always laughing at me—for no reason. It's like they need something to laugh at, and I'm the one who stands out from the crowd, so they laugh at me. Well, I don't exist to play a role for somebody else.

Her smirk says, "You don't fit in. You'll never fit in. You'll never be good enough to fit in."

There's only so much a guy can take before he's just going to snap and shove her so hard that it knocks the smirk right off her face. It worked, too. But then I'm the one who gets suspended. *She* should be suspended. She started it.

But that's okay. I'll be the bad guy. I *am* the bad guy. I don't mind. I kind of like it. And I think I could be really good at it...in time.

So I've started planning some things—some bad things. I don't want anyone to get hurt, but there are plenty of people out there who could stand to feel a little scared—who need a good wake-up call telling them that not everyone fits into their neat little world. Some of us don't even want to fit into it.

For what seemed like the longest time, I had to do all my thinking in my head because my mom is always nosing around in my stuff at home. It wouldn't be safe to keep anything there. But then I had a stroke of good luck: I found a place. It's out in the woods past the railroad tracks. Nobody knows about it. I go out there and make my plans. It's the only thing I look forward to.

The place is a little weird—creepy, actually. But that's okay. I like creepy. I *am* creepy.

It's a cabin. A very old one—so old that it looks like it grew there among the trees. It's shaped like a rectangular box with a pointed roof. Its walls are covered in wooden shingles. It has a door at the front, a gridded-glass window on each side, and a chimney at the back. It's pretty weather-battered, and you can see chinks here and there where the wind probably blows through. But that doesn't matter here in Red River, Louisiana, where it never gets too cold for comfort outside. Too hot, yes, in midsummer. I'll find out in a month or two, but I bet it won't be that bad in the wooded ravine where the cabin is located.

I scoped out the cabin for a few days before going inside because I figured it must belong to someone—some crazy person with a hunting rifle or a bloody hatchet or something. But no one came around. When I dared to creep closer, it seemed pretty clear that the cabin had been abandoned for some time. No muddy footprints. No signs of a campfire. So I opened the front door and looked inside.

It's small—about ten feet by fifteen feet—and pretty empty. There's a bed, a few chairs, a crate of firewood, a small table, and a desk.

"Hello?" I called, knowing there was no one there. There was nowhere for someone to hide. Still, I felt I should announce myself before barging in.

When no one answered, I entered and sat down on the bed. It was really just a cot with a blue-and-white checkered mat and a single, grayish-green wool blanket—the scratchy kind.

Whose hideout is this? I kept thinking to myself, amazed because it was just the sort of hideout I'd have built for myself if I'd had the chance. *Maybe they're done with it, and it can be mine.*

I leaned against the wall behind the cot and took a deep breath—the first really deep, untroubled breath I'd had for a while, actually. The air was tangy and sweet. I heard some skittering in the tree outside the window where I'd observed a family of squirrels. I also heard the high-pitched squeal of some whistling ducks.

The cabin was clean. Well, the wooden floor was dirty, but in a normal way for a cabin in the woods. What I mean is that there was no garbage—like beer cans and chip bags—strewn around. That's part of what made it so eerie. Because there are always beer cans and chip bags, right? I swear, after humans kill themselves off and aliens come to our planet to check it out, they'll think we *lived* for beer and chips.

So that day in mid-May, when I was lounging on the cot—*my* cot—breathing deep, enjoying furtive animal sounds and moist fragrances floating freely through the open door, that's when I first noticed the picture.

It was tacked on the wall above the desk. The predominant colors in it were dark green and brown, just like the mossy wooden wall behind it, which is why I didn't notice it at first. It was a poster print of a professional painting—an old one. I sat staring across the room at it for a long time.

At the center of the painting was a majestic, old tree. It was so tall that even the lowest branches were beyond the top of the painting. Dazzling sunlight fell on its trunk, highlighting the bark's texture. If you looked closely, that trunk almost became a long, thin face—an ancient face, wise and a little bit sad. In the end, I decided that the painting was mostly about this tree.

But the tree wasn't the only thing. There were actually fourteen men standing or sitting beneath it. They had a small tent and a large lean-to. Like a patch of wild mushrooms, they were wearing an interesting assortment of camping hats.

Most of the men—eleven to be exact—were looking at something beyond the right side of the painting. One of the men was aiming a rifle at it, whatever it was. But he wasn't entirely prepared to shoot.

Was it an animal? A bear? A family of deer? Surely not. These men were not hunting. They were at their camp, puzzled by an interruption, thinking about it—about how to respond to it.

The three who weren't paying attention to the thing seemed to be gutting a fish on a large, flat-topped stump. Whether they were studying the fish or getting ready to cook it wasn't clear.

But the rest were transfixed by the thing, and were none too pleased by it. It was something vexing, unexpected. While they weren't exactly afraid of it, they weren't about to go any closer, either. The man in the middle, closest to the wise, old tree, seemed the most ambivalent. You could almost see him turn toward the fish gutters and then back toward the thing and then back again, swiveling in indecision.

A ghost? An alien? A pack of wolves? None of these possibilities seemed to fit.

I racked my brain until I couldn't stand it anymore. I just had to read the fine print at the bottom of the poster. Surely the title of the painting would yield a clue.

https://concordlibrary.org/special-collections/emerson-celebration/Em_Con_80

The painting was called *The Philosophers' Camp*, by William James Stillman.

Leaning against the little desk as I squinted to read the title of the painting, I bumped the handle of a small drawer in it—the only inch of the cabin I had not yet examined. I opened it. Inside was a note written in blue ink on an open notebook that was crispy new and otherwise blank. The note read:

Who are these men,
and what are they looking at?

CHAPTER
TWO

I hustled on out of the cabin after seeing that note. It was just so fresh and deliberate. Obviously someone was still using the desk. I suddenly felt like a fish in a fishbowl—like someone might be scoping *me* out.

Whose land was the cabin on, anyhow? The railroad? The national park? Private property? It wasn't clear from what I could see on the internet.

Dang! I really needed that cabin now. I had already begun putting my plan into action. My plan? Oh yes, my plan.

Well, Memorial Day is coming up, you know, at the end of May. It's a day off from school and from work. Other than that, most people don't bother celebrating. But then there's Mr. Smith.

Daniel Duncan Smith III is what my mom calls a "real doozy." He must weigh about 300 pounds. Most of the time he drives around in one of those fancy wheelchairs, even though he can walk fine when he wants to. He lives alone in an old house on the bayou at the far edge of our neighborhood. My mom says there's no way his property is included in our neighborhood association, but it must be because he has the key—the only key—to the boathouse on our neighborhood pond.

The boathouse on the pond has been a major source of contention ever since I can remember. Every few years it flairs up, and there's a big fight, with people taking sides and arguing up and down the neighborhood social media page. Then people get sick of it and forget about it until the next time.

The issue is that the boathouse is a hideous and useless piece of crap that needs to be torn down, but it can't be torn down because it's legally protected as some kind of "historic building." A couple of years ago when the Ramackers moved into our neighborhood, Mr. Ramacker offered to build a fishing shack with a pier in its place, which would have been awesome. *But nooo.*

The boathouse is so bad that it can't even be used as a hideout. Believe me—I've tried. Even if it wasn't locked with inaccessible windows, the floor is cracked and rotten. It's a miracle that it doesn't simply topple into the water. We all keep hoping it will, but it never does.

Mr. Smith's granddaddy was an army chaplain in the Civil War. Each Memorial Day, Mr. Smith gets a crap-load of fireworks and sets them off from the roof of that old boathouse to commemorate Daniel Duncan Smith I. The crazy thing is that if Daniel Duncan Smith I was a soldier from the Deep South in the Civil War, then he would have been a *Confederate* soldier fighting to *keep* slavery. But Memorial Day was established to celebrate the victory of the Union North, which fought to *end* slavery. So the whole thing is totally messed up. Mr. Smith refuses to talk about it. Not the most talkative guy to begin with, he's especially *untalkative* about Memorial Day.

But the fireworks are always pretty cool. Most of the neighborhood comes out to watch—whether they are ultimately for Mr. Smith or against him. He gets drunk and gets up on that roof and yells his rebel yells and shoots off his fiery rockets. The local law enforcement just looks the other way.

So anyhow, here's my great idea: I'm going to blow the thing up. I'm going to blow that boathouse to smithereens. It's going to be easy because I'm going to do it in true Civil War style, with nothing but black powder.

Black powder was the only known chemical explosive up until the mid- to late nineteenth century. They used it in guns and canons and for blasting tunnels in solid rock. They still use it in fireworks. It's what gives fireworks that distinctive, acrid smell.

Black powder is not as powerful as dynamite, but the beauty of it is that you can make it yourself at home. The only problem is that I'll need a lot of it—I figure about ten pounds. According to my research, ten one-pound containers, strategically placed under the wooden floors of the boathouse, remotely ignited at the same time, should be devastating. That's what I'm aiming for: devastation. Devastation with an audience! It will knock them right off their high horses.

It's not really that dangerous, if you do it right. I mean, you don't want to ingest any of the ingredients or get them in your eyes, so I got safety glasses, a dust mask, and gloves. And you need a ventilated place to work, hence the cabin. *My cabin. Well, the cabin I thought was mine.*

I might have abandoned the whole project after finding the notebook if I hadn't gotten ahead of myself. But I did— I'll admit it. I'd bought the supplies before I found that stupid notebook. *Ugh!*

I was just so sure that the cabin was abandoned. I wanted it to be—needed it to be. I'd ordered all the stuff online and used the boathouse address for delivery so my mom wouldn't see any of it. As the boxes started to arrive, I just swung past the boathouse and put them in a big plastic tub under the porch. No one would ever notice. Even if they did, they would just think it was Mr. Smith's fireworks.

Now here I sit with all the ingredients for a catastrophe and no place to mix them.

I was thinking that thought as I rounded the boathouse, having put the final box in its hiding place. That's when I ran into Ivy.

CHAPTER THREE

Ivy eyed me warily. It had only been about a week and a half since the incident at school—the one in which I'd shoved her and gotten suspended for it. She'd fallen backward—hard—and hit her head on the concrete. I hadn't spoken to her or to the other neighborhood girls since then. I looked away.

There was just one narrow dirt path through the tall weeds along the banks of the pond. Ivy was standing in my way of getting back to the road. I wasn't going to be able to slide past her. But I wasn't going to turn back toward the boathouse, either. I stood my ground and crossed my arms over my chest, braced for the worst.

Ivy put a hand to her forehead to block the rays of the setting sun and squinted at the boathouse. "What are you doing here?" she asked me.

"Nothing," I shot back. "What are *you* doing here?"

Ivy shrugged. "I was going by and saw you at the boathouse, so I thought I'd find out what you were up to."

"I'm not up to anything." I sidestepped off the path into the weeds, making a break for the road, cringing at the thought of the chigger bites I knew would end up on my ankles.

"TJ?" she called to my back.

"What?" I cast a half-hearted glance over my shoulder without slowing down.

"It wasn't me who told." She had her fists planted deep in her hoodie pockets. "I wanted you to know that. Because I fight my own battles."

That stopped me short for a minute. Despite how badly I wanted out of those weeds, I had to turn around and see what expression she had on her face. You can tell a lot by the expression on a person's face. It's something that's hard to fake. Most people aren't born natural actors. Even actors aren't convincing most of the time. From a distance, sure, but if you look real close, you can always tell what they're really thinking.

In fact, I think that's why I pushed her: because I couldn't stand the look on her face at that moment. Overall, I'd always liked Ivy's face. She has freckles and big blue eyes. We grew up in the neighborhood together. We'd climbed trees and caught snakes along with all the other kids. But that changed by the time we got to middle school, and now she's all the time with that pack of snotty girls.

I stood there for a minute and tried to get a fix on Ivy's face. She was too far away for me to tell what she was really thinking.

"Uh, okay," I mumbled. "Thanks?" I started backing away. "I mean, sorry and everything. I didn't mean to push you that hard."

"I know."

A car rattled by on the road. We both automatically turned to look. It was Mr. Smith in his rusty pickup truck. Most of the people who live in our neighborhood wave when they drive by. He's one of the ones who doesn't.

I slapped at a bug on my shin. Then I turned and continued my way out of the weeds. When I got to the road heading for home, I glanced back. Ivy was gone.

Crap. She is so onto me. She's going to tell her friends about my stash, and then they're going to rat me out.

I could feel a cold sweat breaking out on my forehead as I hoofed it home. It was getting dark. I couldn't do anything about it that night, but the next day was Saturday. I made a plan.

First thing in the morning, I would haul my stash down to the cabin. I'd work like a dog, measuring and grinding. I'd work all day if I had to. But the DIY video I'd watched indicated that you could make a pound of black powder in about a half hour. According to that calculation, I could be done in five hours. Then I'd dig a hole in the ground and bury the tub full of containers. It would be fine. I could leave it out there until Memorial Day. And then I'd have my catastrophe.

So that's what I did—more or less. I forgot to allow time for hauling. I had to stuff everything into a backpack, and it wouldn't all fit, so I had to make two trips. Plus, your hands get surprisingly tired from grinding nonstop for such a long time, so I had to take breaks. I quit on Saturday afternoon with only about six pounds made. But I went back Sunday morning and got the job done.

No one came to the cabin all that while.

I stood at the little desk doing my work, listening to the woods and thinking about the *Philosophers' Camp* painting on the wall in front of me.

When at last the tub of containers was safely buried, I was exhausted. I swear I'd never worked so hard for anything before in my entire life. I felt I'd earned a brief repose on my old cot, even if it was for the last time.

I tried to relax, but it just wasn't the same as before, when I'd believed that the cabin was all mine. So I gathered my equipment in my backpack and got ready to leave. On my way out, I checked the note in the drawer. Still there, same as before.

In my haste to flee the other day, however, I'd failed to register that the notebook was not the only thing in the drawer. There was also a leather-bound book called *Walden; or, Life in the Woods*, by someone named Henry David Thoreau.

When I picked it up, a bookmark fell to the floor. It was a tiny dreamcatcher, similar to one I had made in art class years ago, only much more beautiful. Its hoop was about an inch in diameter. Silvery-blue threads were laced across the hoop to form a spiderweb. Three small iridescent feathers hung from the hoop. The whole thing was attached to a silver handle that was supposed to mark the page.

I remember my art teacher telling our class that dreamcatchers originated with Native Americans. According to legend, they used dreamcatchers to protect children from bad dreams, which would get caught in the spiderweb.

I could easily see what page the dreamcatcher had been marking—it had been there so long that it left an indentation. The page was about the house the author had built:

> Before winter I built a chimney, and shingled the sides of my house, which were already impervious to rain, with imperfect and sappy shingles made of the first slice of the log, whose edges I was obliged to straighten with a plane.

> I have thus a tight shingled and plastered house, ten feet wide by fifteen long, and eight-feet posts, with a garret and a closet, a large window on each side, two trap doors, one door at the end, and a brick fireplace opposite. The exact cost of my house, paying the usual

price for such materials as I used, but not counting the work, all of which was done by myself, was as follows; and I give the details because very few are able to tell exactly what their houses cost, and fewer still, if any, the separate cost of the various materials which compose them:—

Boards	$8.03½
	Mostly shanty boards.
Refuse shingles for roof and sides	$4.00
Laths	$1.25
Two second-hand windows with glass	$2.43
One thousand old brick	$4.00
Two casks of lime	$2.40
	That was high.
Hair	$0.31
	More than I needed.
Mantle-tree iron	$0.15
Nails	$3.90
Hinges and screws	$0.14
Latch	$0.10
Chalk	$0.01
Transportation	$1.40
	I carried a good part on my back.
In all	$28.12½

These are all the materials, excepting the timber, stones, and sand, which I claimed by squatter's right. I have also a small woodshed adjoining, made chiefly of the stuff which was left after building the house.

According to its title page, the book was published in 1854. Adjusting for more than a century and a half of inflation, the guy's house would still have had to cost less than a thousand dollars.

Flipping through the book before I put it back, this sentence caught my eye:

> In short, I am convinced, both by faith and experience, that to maintain one's self on this earth is not a hardship but a pastime, if we will live simply and wisely....

Hustling on home, I did my best to forget about the cabin by playing video games for the rest of the day. But that night I had the strangest dream.

CHAPTER
FOUR

I was on some kind of bus, lumbering along over a dirt road. But it wasn't a bus; it was a wooden coach. Leaning out the window, I could see that we were being pulled by a team of horses. Six people, in addition to myself, sat on the two scantily padded benches inside the coach. Next to me was a middle-aged, dark-haired woman in a full-length blue dress. Next to her were two old men. Across from us were three businessmen dressed in black suits with shiny top hats.

This was not my normal life. This was the nineteenth century.

I was holding a satchel on my lap. Inside were papers indicating that my name was Frederick "Llew" Llewellyn Hovey Willis. I was fifteen years old. I was an orphan being raised by my grandmother. I was a good student, destined for nearby Harvard University in a few years. I was on my way to Still River Village to board with the Smith family for the summer.

It wasn't exactly the kind of dream I would have chosen for myself if I'd had a choice. On the other hand, the dream was remarkably vivid and absorbing—like a good movie. Unable to wake myself, I decided to play along, to the point that I began to forget that the whole thing was just a dream.

"Excuse me, ma'am," I said to the woman sitting next to me. "Do you know how long before we reach Still River?"

"Hmm." She took a small round clock out of her handbag, flipped it open, and squinted at its Roman numerals. "We're about a half hour from my stop in Concord, and Still River is about three hours past that." She smiled sympathetically, seeing that I was a bit green around the gills from the bumpy ride. She introduced herself as Mrs. Alcott, and I introduced myself as Llew.

Before either of us had the chance to say another word, we lurched to a stop, and the two old men, who had been dozing, roused themselves and prepared to disembark. The driver swung down from his perch behind the horses and placed a stepping stool under the door, but he did not linger to lend a hand. The first old man stumbled on his way to the ground and nearly fell. When I saw that the second old man was no steadier on his feet than the first, and that the adjacent businessman was too busy reading his newspaper to care, I rose to help as best I could.

"Thank you, lad," the second old man grunted after landing safely on the ground. Then he stood with his arms outstretched, gazing past me, toward the roof of the carriage. There was a young black man up there, holding up a suitcase.

"Dis be de one?" the young man asked.

"Yes," the old man confirmed, "and the small black trunk next to it, too."

"Yessuh," said the young man, handing it down.

As I listened to this exchange, I sank back down onto the coach bench. Unfortunately, I was still gripping the narrow frame that separated the window from the door. When the old man paused to shut the door of the coach, he slammed it right on my fingers.

"Owww!" I howled, yanking my hand back and pressing my throbbing fingers to my mouth. (And here's where I realized that this dream was unlike any dream I had ever had before, since I had never felt real pain in a dream.)

The three businessmen looked up at me, frowning in annoyance.

"Oh, sweet mercy!" Mrs. Alcott exclaimed. "Is it broken?" She slid across the bench to me, instinctively smoothing my floppy hair out of my face as if I were a child of her own. Then she gently pried my injured hand free from my other hand to examine it.

Meanwhile, the young man who had been on the roof burst into the carriage. His eyes were wide, his mouth open, terrified that my injury was somehow his fault. "Is de gemmen huwit?" he gasped.

Before Mrs. Alcott could answer, the driver returned from relieving himself in the bushes and took in the scene. "What kina trouble you causin', nigga?" he bellowed at the young man, who had backed out of the carriage in haste.

The young man shook his head, stammering, speechless. The two old men were already walking away, oblivious, focused on the next leg of their journey.

The driver took a pistol out of his pocket and brandished it at the young man. "Git outta here. Go on!"

The young man raised his hands in protest, but that only alarmed the driver. He shot his pistol into the sky as a warning. Mrs. Alcott screamed, throwing her arms around me protectively. The young man grabbed his bundle from the roof and ran off.

The three businessmen looked on with expressions ranging from impatience to discomfort to dismay.

When he was sure that the young man was gone, the driver poked his head into the carriage and addressed Mrs. Alcott. "I beg your pardon, ma'am. Are you all right?"

"You were too quick to blame." Mrs. Alcott pointed to my hand. "*This* was the injury, and it was *not* that young man's fault."

The driver was not interested in getting to the bottom of the matter. "Anyhow," he grunted, "we'll be moving on now."

The first businessman shook his head in disgust. "Never help a freed slave," he pronounced to his fellow passengers as the coach rumbled forward again.

"These parts are crawling with them," the second businessman observed.

The third nodded grimly. "It's only going to get worse until they outlaw slavery in the South."

"How are they going to do that?" the first scoffed. "Their whole economy depends on slave labor. What we need is a decent fugitive slave law."

"We don't really know whether that man was a fugitive or a freedman," the second businessman pointed out.

"Make it illegal to help fugitives, and no one will help any of 'em," the first snarled. "They all lie about their credentials anyhow. I say we send 'em back to wherever they came from."

Mrs. Alcott, already on high alert from the incident, was growing increasingly agitated by the conversation. "You gentlemen have no compassion," she scolded. Her voice was strained and unsteady. "Now shush your mouths so this injured boy can have some peace."

My hand was bleeding. I could barely wiggle my pinky finger. Mrs. Alcott wrapped her embroidered handkerchief around the wound as best she could and told me a long story in a gentle voice about the time her daughter Louisa May broke her ankle jumping out of a tree.

"That girl is stubborn as an old cow," she chuckled.

I sniffed bravely.

"Listen, Llew," Mrs. Alcott commanded, fixing her big, brown eyes on mine. "I cannot send you on to Still River in your present condition. We are coming up on Concord in just a few minutes. We need to get you off this coach and bandaged properly. My four girls are good nurses. You'll see. You must come to our house."

"I'm expected at the Smith residence," I countered, "where I'm to board for the summer."

"Oh!" Mrs. Alcott grimaced. "The Smiths. I used to live in Still River, and I know just who they are." A look of determination stole over her face, suggesting where her daughter might have gotten her stubborn streak. "We'll send word to the Smiths that you'll be staying with us until you're well enough to move on."

To pass the remaining time to Concord, Mrs. Alcott shared her magazine with me. It contained a strange article called "Orphic Sayings" by her husband, Bronson Alcott.

CHAPTER
FIVE

ORPHIC SAYINGS
by Bronson Alcott

ENTHUSIASM.
Believe, young people, that your heart is an oracle! Trust its instinctive judgments. Do not listen to the uncertain echoes in your head. Listen to your heart—it is big with future possibilities. Let its enthusiastic flame glow brightly in your chest. Enthusiasm is the true source of all hope.

HOPE.
Hope makes human beings divine. It is the noblest aspiration of the soul—the fulfillment of its destiny. The nobler your aspiration, the more sublime your conception of God. However you are, that is how your God is. God is your idea of excellence, the complement of your own being.

IMMORTALITY.
The more excellent my conception of God, the nobler my future. Let me live above sensation and custom, and I shall experience my divinity. My hope will be infinite so that the universe can neither contain nor content me. Those who guide their own growth and believe all things possible partake of the eternity of God.

SOLITUDE.

Solitude is wisdom's school. Attend to the lessons of your own soul. Become a student of the wise God within you. This is the only way to discover divine knowledge. It is as though angels descend from heaven during the solitude of meditation.

CONSCIENCE.

Ever-present in your chest there is something that has never been a party to your wrongdoing. It is the deity of your heart, otherwise known as your conscience. This oracle is the judge and executor of the divine law.

THEOCRACY.

In the theocracy of the soul, majorities do not rule. Majorities clamor against divine law, silencing the oracle of their hearts. Majorities obey Beelzebub. Majorities are always the special enemies of prophets and reformers. Majorities always lie. Every age is a Judas and betrays its Messiahs into the hands of the majority. The speech of the private heart, though not popular, is alone authentic.

SPEECH.

There is a magic in free speech, especially on sacred themes. It is refreshing, amidst so many tired clichés, to hear a hopeful word from an earnest, upright soul. Free speech is like a breeze from the mountains, invigorating sleepy people. On hearing it, they feel a buoyant sense of health, and they wonder why they slept so long. Free speech charms, exalts, and teaches.

TEACHER.

The true teacher protects his students from his own personal influence. He inspires them to trust themselves. He guides their eyes away from himself toward the spirit that moves him. He will have no disciples. A noble artist, he shares visions of excellence and revelations of beauty. Individuals study his life and teachings for yet nobler ideals.

INDIVIDUALS.

Individuals are sacred. Creeds and institutions are sacred only insofar as they revere the individual. The world, the State, the Church, and the school are criminal whenever they violate the sanctity of the private heart. The human individual is divine—mightier and holier than any societal power.

CHRISTENDOM.

Christendom is infidel. It violates the sanctity of a person's conscience. It does not speak from the inspiration of the soul but instead reads from society's traditions. It quotes history, not life. It denounces the intuitions of the individual as heresy. By denying that conscience is God, Christians condemn the prophet Jesus as arch-heretic.

When I finished reading, I glanced at Mrs. Alcott. She was waiting for my reaction.

I could feel my face contorting with doubt. "Beelzebub?"

She cringed. "It's a fancy word for the devil. Sometimes Bronson is a little over-the-top with his poetic language." Silence descended upon us.

"Well, I like what he said about teachers," I offered at last. "I guess I'll have to think about the rest."

She arched her eyebrows. "That's a lot kinder and more generous than the reaction of most people—even the other

Transcendentalists." She did a double-take. "Are you a Transcendentalist, Llew?"

I shrugged. "What's a Transcendentalist?"

"Oh." Her eyes twinkled. "Well, you'll find out."

CHAPTER
SIX

Concord was a tiny town scattered across a blanket of leafy, green hills. When our coach pulled up in front of the Alcotts' two-story farmhouse, four girls dropped the laundry they were hanging out to dry and ran to meet us.

The two youngest, with blonde hair pulled into long braids, threw themselves at their mother's skirts the moment she disembarked. Mrs. Alcott bent to kiss them with gusto on each cheek. Then she hugged the two older girls.

"I missed you so much!" she murmured, lost for a moment in a wave of family love. "Well, come on, girls. Meet our guest."

The Alcott sisters eyed me uncertainly as I stepped off the stagecoach behind Mrs. Alcott. I was supposed to be from Cambridge, Massachusetts, I knew, from the papers in my satchel. My clothes—not overly fancy, but store-bought— set me apart from the girls, in their homemade muslin frocks.

We had an awkward moment of introductions. The two little girls were Lizzie and Abby May. The oldest, statuesque with her blonde hair smoothed into a tight bun, was Anna. The second-oldest, her dark, unfastened hair tangling in the fitful summer breeze, was Lou.

"Your name is Lou, too?" she exclaimed.

I nodded. "But I bet we spell it differently because my 'Llew' is short for Llewellyn. What's yours short for?"

"Louisa. Louisa May, actually."

As soon as she said that, I knew just who she was: Louisa May Alcott, the author of the classic novel *Little Women*. We had just watched the movie in English class. *Little Women* is basically a soap opera about four girls and their mother, loosely based on Louisa May Alcott's real life. Although it was a runaway hit in the nineteenth century, it was way too girly for me. Why was I dreaming about this?

We proceeded into the house. But whose house was it: Mrs. Alcott's or her daughters'? It looked as though the latter were at least in charge of the furnishings. The living room floor was scattered with oversized pillows and colorful rugs. Amateur artwork was tacked on every wall. A set of hand-built shelves contained piles of dilapidated books and dog-eared papers. In one corner, some sort of theater had been constructed out of poles and mismatched curtains. On a well-worn coffee table stood a copper statue of an old man in a toga. I recognized him, but couldn't think of his name until I read the inscription: Socrates.

The girls sat me down at the dining room table. Two of them undertook the task of fashioning a splint for my injured hand, while the other two helped Mrs. Alcott prepare refreshments. Amidst this flurry of activity, they threw a lot of questions at me, many of which I didn't know how to answer: *What is Cambridge like? Do you attend a big school there? What's your favorite subject? Do you go to plays and concerts? Do you study philosophy? What do you intend to do with your life?*

Mrs. Alcott had just finished pouring tea for everyone when a man with overgrown, scraggly sideburns thumped down the stairs. He was startled by the noisy scene he interrupted, as though he thought for a moment that he was in the wrong house, or maybe even on the wrong planet.

Mrs. Alcott stood and introduced the man as her husband, Bronson Alcott. Having read his strange *Orphic Sayings*, I was nervous to meet him. His daughters sat mutely without touching their cucumber sandwiches, waiting for their father's pronouncement on the situation. I rose slowly from my chair, which was plainly *his* chair at the head of the table.

Mr. Alcott listened intently to his wife's explanation of my circumstances. As she concluded, his face lit up with a broad smile. "Welcome, son." Mr. Alcott drew near and took my good hand in both of his. "It is a great honor to have you here as our guest. Though we are humble people, we love good company. Please make yourself at home."

There weren't enough chairs for everyone. Mr. Alcott bade me sit back down and retrieved a battered crate from the kitchen for himself. Though the crate was lower than the chairs, it put him at eye level with the rest of us because he was so tall. Once he was seated, everyone started eating.

"Do you attend public school in Cambridge, good sir?" Mr. Alcott asked me.

I nodded, helping myself to a fresh-baked cinnamon biscuit.

"Ah," he sighed. "My condolences. Your soul will take much longer to heal than will your hand. You may need to stay here a while."

I must have shown some puzzlement at this remark. Louisa May piped up to explain. "My father believes that traditional schools are bad for students." She popped a handful of wild blackberries into her mouth and continued to speak with her mouth full. "He started an experimental school in Boston that was different."

"Different how?" I asked.

Louisa May deferred to her father.

Mr. Alcott speared a tomato with his fork and held it up for everyone admire. "Just look at this work of art," he marveled. "Nature's perfect bounty. A few months ago, it was entirely contained in a puny little seed. That seed burst to life out of ordinary dirt. First it became a plant; then it produced flowers; then they bore fruit. This glorious tomato needed nothing but a daily dose of sunshine and water to develop its unique color, shape, and flavor. Children are exactly the same way. They come with their own unique characteristics built in. All they need is some fresh air and a daily dose of sunshine."

I drew the inference. "You feel that traditional schools are too restrictive."

"Being forced to sit still indoors and listen to someone else all day long stunts growth rather than promoting it," Mr. Alcott replied. "Traditional schools are designed to break your spirit. *Break* your spirit and replace it with something else." On the word *break*, Mr. Alcott slammed his tomato down on the table, smashing it and spraying juice in every direction. "Break it and replace it with someone else's idea of what you should be."

Mrs. Alcott, embarrassed by her husband's outburst, retrieved a rag from the kitchen to wipe up his mess.

Abby May, the youngest sister, turned her wide blue eyes to me. "Do the teachers beat you a lot at your school, Mr. Llew?"

My mouth fell open in surprise at such a shocking question. But as I studied the serene curiosity on Abby May's face, mirrored by her family members all around the table, it dawned on me that corporal punishment was the norm in nineteenth-century schools.

"Well, not so much," I hedged, "because I mostly do as I'm told. I guess maybe my spirit is already broken."

"Well, with your mother and father both dead, who could blame you?" Mrs. Alcott cooed.

I nodded modestly. "But I do stay up past bedtime to read. I use candles I bought by selling junk I find."

Abby May grew excited by this confession. "And your grandmother don't never knowed it?!'"

I grinned. "Nope."

Abby May and Lizzie clapped enthusiastically, hoping for more.

I combed my memory for details from the letter I'd read from my satchel. "Well, my grandmother didn't know about it until she caught me, and that's why she's sending me away to the Smiths. She says she's too frail to discipline me properly."

"What books do you read by candlelight, Llew?" Louisa May asked. "Do you read *Robinson Crusoe* and *The Swiss Family Robinson*?"

I nodded slyly, groping for another title that would have been available to a fifteen-year-old boy in the nineteenth century. "And Shakespeare," I added.

Mr. Alcott beamed. "At our school, the children would read all those things, and play outside, and write about themselves in journals, and they were never, ever beaten. And that's why we were shut down."

"I thought it was because you admitted a colored student," Anna countered.

"Well," Mr. Alcott sighed, "there was that, too. There were a lot of things. So I'm done trying to run a school! Llew, I've been sending my girls to my best friend Henry David Thoreau for lessons. You can meet him tomorrow."

CHAPTER
SEVEN

As luck would have it, Mr. Alcott was in the process of building an addition onto the house. The new room was actually half of an old shed that he was attaching. Mrs. Alcott set up a bed of blankets for me on its floor. As the walls were still unfinished, sleeping there wasn't much better than camping, but since the night was warm, it didn't matter.

I wondered how it would work going to sleep in a dream. Would I have dreams within the dream? When I woke up in the dream, would I wake up to real life again?

As it turned out, neither of those things happened. I simply shut my eyes, and when I opened them again, it was morning at the Alcott home.

My hand was so much better that I felt a bit foolish for allowing my hosts to make such a fuss over it. I decided not to take the splint off, though, since I had no desire to move on to Still River.

I'll confess: I was hoping for an old-fashioned farm breakfast of fried eggs and bacon. When I arrived in the dining room, however, I found only fruit and bread laid out on the table. Louisa May, who was feeding a crust of bread to a cat, explained that her family did not believe in eating animals or animal products.

Mr. Alcott was already out working in the garden. Mrs. Alcott brought me one of his shirts to wear and said that she would work on altering a pair of trousers to fit me. I noticed then that I was wearing the same thing I had worn the day before. But so were the girls.

I frowned. "I have a change of clothes in my trunk."

"Llew," she sighed. "It's just that your clothes are made from cotton, which was picked by slaves in the South. All cotton comes from slavery. Wouldn't you rather have muslin?"

"Oh." An image popped into my mind: a woman and two children with baskets slung around their shoulders in a field under the hot sun. Bending and crouching. Pulling handfuls of fluffy white stuff from scraggly plants. Dark skin. Rags wrapped around their heads. The children crying, and the woman singing a sad, sad song. "Yes," I said. "I would."

Mrs. Alcott blushed and busied herself cutting apple slices.

I hustled back to my room to put the linen shirt on. I was looking forward to meeting the girls' teacher, Henry David Thoreau. I figured he had to be the whole point of this dream, which must have stemmed from the book I had found in the desk drawer at the cabin: *Walden; or, Life in the Woods*, by Henry David Thoreau. Though I hadn't recognized his name at first, my subconscious mind had apparently put together that he was Louisa May Alcott's teacher. I'd probably heard that during some boring lecture at school.

Perhaps my subconscious mind was trying to convey a theory about why that book was in the drawer. I pictured the book and the accompanying notebook entry concerning the painting hanging on the wall above the desk:

Who are these men,
and what are they looking at?

Then I pictured the men in the painting. None of those men had the overgrown sideburns of Mr. Bronson Alcott. Or was *he* the thing the men were looking at? I hoped that the meeting with Henry David Thoreau would clue me in.

It was a blustery morning. Mrs. Alcott sent us out with coats and lunch pails. I had pictured walking to some little schoolhouse in town to meet Thoreau, but it turned out that Thoreau was really just an informal tutor and met with the girls at his house, about two miles away.

Louisa May explained: "Mr. Thoreau tried to work as a traditional schoolteacher, but he got fired for refusing to beat the children. So he started a school with his brother that was a lot like my father's. But when his brother died, Thoreau just couldn't carry on with it. He got...well, fed up with everything and went to live in the woods."

It was just Louisa May and I walking on a well-worn path into the countryside. The younger sisters, Lizzie and Abby May, were deemed too young for lessons outside the home, and the oldest sister, Anna, was working as a seamstress for the summer, which would bring much-needed income to the family.

"So Thoreau lives out in the woods all alone?" I asked.

Louisa May nodded. "In a cabin he built himself for twenty-eight dollars and twelve and a half cents."

Ah yes. I recalled the page I had read in his book.

Suddenly realizing that Louisa May was no longer next to me, I stopped walking and turned to look back. She had paused to pick wildflowers in the tall grass. I waited.

She rearranged her bouquet in deep concentration. "You might think that Thoreau went out to the woods because he was depressed about his brother. But it wasn't that—or at least, it wasn't *just* that. It was bigger than that. He was depressed about how people fritter away their lives working to earn more and more money for bigger and better houses and stuff, and then they die without ever having really lived."

I nodded, thinking about how my parents had been fighting about the fact that my mom wants to hire a cleaning lady because our expensive house is too big for her to clean all the time.

Louisa May continued. "Thoreau says that the mass of men lead lives of quiet desperation. The only answer is to simplify, simplify, simplify. If you don't spend all your time wanting things you don't need, then you have time to enjoy yourself."

"Huh." I tried to picture how I would enjoy myself if I didn't have video games. Nothing came to mind.

Louisa May made me be quiet for the rest of the walk so that she could listen for birds. Thoreau's last homework assignment for her was to describe the difference between the call of the bittern and the call of the heron.

"How am I supposed to know?" she complained.

"And who cares?" I added sympathetically.

Halfway to Walden, we skirted another pond called Fairyland. Sitting on the glassy surface of the water was a bird with a long, curved neck. Louisa May froze, thinking it might be a heron. But it flew away without making any call for us.

After we slogged around a giant willow tree, Louisa May caught my arm. "We've arrived," she whispered, pointing to a cabin that looked just like "my" cabin in real-life Louisiana. "Be very quiet," she added. "Mr. Thoreau gets angry when you scare away his little friends."

I screwed up my face, signaling for further explanation. Hopefully Thoreau was not a crazy person. But Louisa May just put her finger to her lips.

As we crept closer, we spotted a man prone in the mud at the edge of the pond. He was lying so still and in such an unnatural position that he had to be dead.

CHAPTER EIGHT

But he wasn't dead. It was Henry David Thoreau. He was making observations of the shoreline to record in his journal.

"Come help me," he urged after we made our introductions. He was short with droopy eyes. His chin was framed by a neckbeard. He spoke with a faint, unidentifiable accent.

Louisa May dove into the mud with no further prompting. I frowned, trying to figure out how to do it without getting dirty.

"You're trying to figure out how to do this without getting dirty, aren't you," Thoreau observed, propping himself on one elbow and cocking an eyebrow at me. Mud was smeared across his face, accentuating his long nose. His thick, auburn hair was standing up in random waves.

"You must have gone to a traditional school." Thoreau frowned at me thoughtfully. "Well, think of it this way: Dirt is part of nature, and nature is part of God, and God is pure. So by getting dirty, you're really purifying yourself."

Louisa May giggled at Thoreau's logic, even though he spoke with a straight face.

Thoreau turned back onto his belly and began counting something or other that was invisible to me. Louisa May started making mud cakes. Thoreau challenged her to find ten distinct lifeforms in the mud.

Louisa May sighed. "I was hoping to learn something *useful* today."

Thoreau laughed and then raised a finger in admonition. "It is only when we forget all our learning that we begin to *know*."

Louisa May harrumphed and started digging around half-heartedly. About an hour later, after she and I together had come up with a list of ten mud-dwellers, we trooped up the hill to Thoreau's cabin to rinse off using a barrel full of rainwater and a dipper.

Louisa May and I dried ourselves on a rag that was hanging from a tree branch while Thoreau went into his cabin and came out with a flute. Perching on his front step, he played a Scottish jig called "I Used to Be a Nice Boy."

Before long, we heard scurrying sounds under a pile of dried leaves. Then a tiny, pointed face popped up and looked around. It was a brown field mouse with large round ears and a fuzzy white torso. Thoreau stopped playing and gave the mouse—"Krishna"—a piece of dried corn from his pocket.

We watched Krishna nibble the corn. When he was finished, he jumped up on Thoreau's lap and scurried around, looking for more. Thoreau sat still and teased Krishna with his finger. When Krishna grew tired of the game, Thoreau tossed a handful of corn to the ground in front of us. This gesture—which seemed like a daily routine—prompted a family of bushy-tailed squirrels out of hiding.

Louisa May did a hilarious imitation of the mother squirrel scolding her children. The children chased one another, diving, pouncing, and somersaulting into the thick carpet of pine needles.

All the squirrel action attracted several birds. They fought for the corn more seriously than did the squirrels. Thoreau identified each type of bird: blue jays, sparrows, and woodcocks. He told us about the interesting survival strategies that he had observed among them. For example, when he got too close to the woodcock nest, the mother would pretend to have a broken wing to lure him away long enough for her chicks to escape though the bushes.

As his furry and feathered friends retreated to the woods with their treats, Thoreau's attention was drawn to the log on which Louisa May and I sat.

"What are you looking at?" I asked.

"Ants."

That got both Louisa May and me up on our feet in a hurry.

"It's an all-out war—black ants versus red ants," Thoreau remarked, pointing to the busy insects that Louisa May and I had failed to notice. "I check in on them almost every day. The black ants are nearly twice as big, but there aren't as many of them. I don't know what these two fierce races are fighting over. Whatever it is, they must think it most important."

Squatting, Thoreau pulled aside a shaft of grass next to the log, revealing piles of dead and wounded ants of both kinds. Louisa May emitted a low whistle.

I was watching a black ant on a branch of the log nearest me. As he marched along with a red ant in his jaws, another red ant jumped him from behind, latching onto his enemy's leg. The black ant flailed wildly, but the red ant would not let go. Soon the tangle of bodies tumbled off the log.

Thoreau played a rousing rendition of "Yankee Doodle" on his flute while Louisa May and I continued to watch. It was gruesome and fascinating at the same time.

"There's food enough for everyone, gentlemen," Louisa May murmured to the tiny soldiers.

"They are just like men," Thoreau agreed when he finished his tune. "The more you think of it, the less the difference."

With a wave of his arm, Thoreau invited us into his cabin. It was furnished exactly the same way as "my" cabin back in real life: a small cot with a scratchy blanket, a desk, a table, and three chairs. Did I lack imagination? Did my mind run short on "dream furnishings"? Or was there a connection between Thoreau's cabin in nineteenth-century Concord, Massachusetts, and its twin in modern-day Red River, Louisiana? The only thing missing was the painting on the wall.

"It's time for our poetry lesson, students," Thoreau proclaimed, laying his flute on the desk in exchange for a piece of paper.

"That's more like it!" exclaimed Louisa May.

"Young lady," Thoreau protested, "I have observed how you take every opportunity to broadcast your strong preference for language arts over science. But those categories are the absurd constructs of unenlightened minds. To love nature is to know her, which is to study her and to celebrate her. Our measurements and our poems must all stem from the same reverent intimacy."

Louisa May scowled stubbornly.

"At any rate," Thoreau continued, "I have here for you a freshly penned poem by Concord's own poet-in-residence, Larry Channing." Thoreau handed us the sheet of paper to read for ourselves.

A Poet's Hope

Lady—
There's one old hope all mortals have:
Some mercy and a resting place,
A daisy-strewn and grassy grave.
But does this hope improve our race?
No, Ma'am—
I seek no resting place for good;
I'm onward to the farthest shores.
So lift me up, unceasing flood,
Which from the purest fountain pours.
I smile, for new hope grows in me:
If my boat sinks, tis to another sea.

Thoreau handed us a pencil and a sheet of paper. "I'd like you to write an analysis of the poem together."

Louisa May and I studied Channing's poem intently and discussed it while Thoreau busied himself outside building and lighting a fire in his fire pit.

Here's what we wrote:

This is a rhythmic, rhyming poem. It is written primarily in iambic tetrameter: most lines follow the pattern of four iambic feet (an unstressed syllable followed by a stressed syllable, repeated four times). The first line and the sixth line provide contrast, consisting of just two syllables of equal stress. The last line also sets itself apart by following iambic pentameter (five iambic feet). The poem's rhyme scheme is A BCBC D EFEF GG.

We think that this poem is about death. Channing notes that everyone hopes for a final "resting place." This makes us think of the common inscription on tombstones: R.I.P., meaning "rest in peace." But Channing never wants to rest in peace. He hopes for a "flood" to bear him forever onward and upward. Since the poem is called "A Poet's Hope," this flood must be the inspiration of poetry. So perhaps he is hoping that poetry will give him some kind of immortality.

Channing addresses the poem to "Lady." Who is she? She must be poetry personified. In line six, he addresses her again as "ma'am." In line nine, it seems that he is asking her to lift him up and carry him away in her flood. However, if it is true that Channing wishes to personify poetry, then line ten should start with *who*, not *which*, since *who* is the pronoun for people, while *which* is the pronoun for things. So either the poet made a grammatical mistake, or the "Lady" is not the poetic flood but someone else.

When we finished writing our analysis, Thoreau was washing his hands in the pond. We walked down the slope to give it to him. He smiled when he read it, pleased.

"So which is it?" Louisa May demanded.

"Which is what?" Thoreau was leading us back to the cabin with a kettle full of lake water.

"Did Channing make a grammatical mistake, or is 'Lady' someone else?" Louisa May clarified.

"I'm not sure." Thoreau stopped and turned to face us. His expression hardened. "Channing has his moments—sublime moments. Like the last line of the poem: 'If my boat sinks, tis to another sea.' That line is true genius. However, Channing is also, well, slipshod, both as a poet and as a man."

"What do you mean by *slipshod*?" I asked.

But Thoreau was done with the poetry lesson. He was already bent on something else. He got down on his knees and yanked open a trapdoor in the middle of the floor of his cabin.

C H A P T E R
N I N E

A pole extended down from the hole in the floor. It was actually the trunk of a medium-sized tree. While its main purpose seemed to be to hold up the floor, footholds chopped into its bark provided a ladder down.

"Oh, wow," I exclaimed. "Cool hiding place."

Thoreau glared at me. "Why would you call it a hiding place? It's just a root cellar. I grow potatoes, beans, radishes, and a few other things. This space keeps them from freezing in the winter and from rotting in the summer."

I nodded apologetically, reminding myself to do a better job of staying in character.

"Farmers slave over giant fields of cash crops," Thoreau continued, "when a simple yard garden yields more than enough. My experiment here at Walden Pond proves it."

He descended into the cellar like a pirate into the hold of his ship. When he reached bottom, his head was only about a foot and a half beneath the floor. But then he ventured several feet into the darkness.

"Can I come down?" I called.

"No!" Thoreau reappeared with a burlap sack. "I'm just bringing up a bag o' 'evil. *Foutu voleur!*"

I did a double-take. "Excuse me?"

Thoreau threw the sack up to me. I jumped back, letting it fall to the floor.

He frowned. "It's dried peas. They're infected with 'evil."

I looked to Louisa May for help with this bizarre turn in the conversation.

"He's saying *weevil*, not *evil*, Llew." She picked up the bag and peered inside. "Weevil are little brownish bugs. See?" She held the bag for me to look, but I declined.

"If I don't eat those peas soon, the wwwweevil will." Thoreau over-pronounced the *w* this time to be sure I heard him right. "If the weevil eat my peas, then I'll have to eat the weevil!"

I grimaced, suspecting that he was serious.

As Thoreau climbed his way out of the root cellar, he caught his foot on a protruding nail and tore the leather of his shoe.

"Tarnation!" he hissed, plunking down on the floor to take stock of the damage. "Well, I can't fix this. Looks like I'll need to pay ol' Jonas a visit."

Louisa May looked up from something she was reading at the table and gave Thoreau a maternal frown. "Do you have any money to pay for the repair?"

Thoreau nodded. "I have four cents left over from the sale of surplus crops last year. But Jonas would probably do the work in exchange for a few pounds of fresh-picked strawberries."

Just then we heard a low, booming sound. Thoreau froze.

"Louisa May," he whispered, "did you hear that?"

Louisa May cocked her head, listening.

"Do you know what that booming sound is?" Thoreau whispered.

"The call of a bittern?" Louisa May hazarded.

"Excellent!" Thoreau exclaimed. "You see? I'll make a naturalist of you yet."

"I learned that from this poem of yours, Mr. Thoreau," Louisa May corrected. She began reading aloud from the paper in her hand:

The Mist

Low-wandering cloud,
dream-drapery for cattails and violets:
through your fairy labyrinth
bitterns boom and herons veer.
Spirit of lakes and seas and rivers—
bring perfume
and the scent of healing herbs
to sorrow-sown fields, both far and near.

"Oh, yes. 'Bitterns boom.'" Thoreau rolled his eyes in chagrin. "Well, anyhow, by Monday I'd like to see if you are able to imitate the call of the heron—the night heron."

"If I do that," Louisa May negotiated, "will you teach me how to be a philosopher? I want to understand the subtle thoughts of Transcendentalism."

Thoreau chuckled. Then he grew serious and raised his finger again in admonition. "Being a philosopher isn't just about having subtle thoughts. Nor is it necessarily about a movement, like Transcendentalism. To be a philosopher is to love wisdom so much that you live according to its dictates: a life of simplicity, magnanimity, and trust. It is to solve some of the problems of life—not only theoretically, but practically."

"But what does the night heron have to do with solving problems?" Louisa May demanded.

Thoreau fixed her with a penetrating gaze. "We never can tell what surprises nature has in store for us."

Louisa May groaned. "I think it's time for us to be on our way. But I love these poems! May I make copies?"

Thoreau shrugged. "As long as you realize that these are not the final drafts. I'd be interested to hear what your father thinks of them."

Seeing as Thoreau had no copy machine in his cabin, Louisa May had to copy the poems by hand. When she finished, she stood, and we bid goodbye to her tutor.

"I guess I'll see you tomorrow at the Saturday symposium," Thoreau sighed. "If I have to come to town to get my shoe fixed anyhow, I may as well stay to enjoy some of Lidian's cooking."

"Oh!" Louisa May recalled. "At Emerson's house."

"Rumor has it that William James Stillman will be there." Thoreau's nose twitched as though he suddenly smelled a foul odor. "And that Stillman will be proposing a camping trip."

"Interesting," Louisa May returned. "We'll see you there!"

Rather than heading home, Louisa May led me across the meadow to another pond, called Crosby, where we could eat our lunches. Crosby Pond was fed by a sparkling waterway called Mill Brook. We took off our shoes and waded against the icy current until we came to a rocky glen that was carpeted with moss and adorned with ferns.

"How about here?" she proposed. "I'm hungry."

I shrugged compliantly and sat down on a flat rock abutting a fallen oak tree. Sunlight filtered through a thick ceiling of leaves. The brook burbled merrily. Crickets sang. Watching Louisa May brush her tangled hair from her face, I felt nature, poetry, and friendship flowing through me. It was a new feeling. I decided I liked it.

"This will be *our* place," I proclaimed.

"And we shall call it Spiderland," Louisa May added, plucking a daddy longlegs off the rock.

Though I didn't really want to look at the spider up close, she was determined to show it to me. "Llew, promise you won't tell anyone about Spiderland. It will be our secret."

I promised.

We ate walnuts and raspberry jam sandwiches. Louisa May talked all the while about the Royal Theater of Spiderland. We would perform great poems and plays for the royal trees that gathered around our stage. We would write masterpieces for future generations. While I lacked Louisa May's literary ambition, I enjoyed her enthusiasm. And something about her seemed so familiar.

When we finished eating, we built a cairn out of stones from the brook to mark our special place. While Louisa May decorated it with the wildflowers she had picked, I used a chalky stone to write "The Royal Stage of Spiderland" on our flat rock.

Louisa May stood tall on the Royal Stage and recited the poems she'd copied to the trees. She was riveting, despite a dribble of raspberry jam on her chin. (I didn't have the heart to tell her.)

"What's that on the back of the page?" I asked after she had taken her final bow.

"Huh?" She turned the page over, and together we read six lines of a poem sketched in pencil:

> Surely, surely, thou wilt trust me
> When I say thou dost disgust me.
> O, I hate thee with a hate
> That would fain annihilate;
> Yet sometimes against my will,
> My dear E, I love thee still.
> If thou won't s

"It cuts off in the middle," Louisa May observed.

"Do you think Thoreau wrote it?" I asked.

"Of course!" She studied the page as though she had just discovered a treasure map. "It's his handwriting."

"About whom?" I asked.

"I'm not sure," she mused, "but maybe it explains why he isn't in the painting."

I did a double-take. "In the *what*?"

"Oh, no!" Louisa May's free hand flew to cover her mouth. "I wasn't supposed to say that!"

Then Spiderland faded out, and I found myself waking up in my modern room, in my modern house, in the modern world.

CHAPTER
TEN

All day Monday at school, I couldn't stop thinking about my dream. I glided from class to class even less alert than usual.

Scientists tell us that we dream every night. Dreams occur during the "rapid eye movement" phase of sleep, when our eyeballs are moving around under our eyelids as though they're seeing things. People typically have several cycles of rapid eye movement during an eight- to nine-hour period of sleep. But most of the time, I don't remember my dreams. When I do, I only remember fleeting glimpses. First I forget details, and then, in a short while, I forget the whole thing.

It wasn't that way at all with my nineteenth-century dream. The memory of my visit to Concord was as vivid as the memory of making those ten black powder bombs. It was like I had actually been there.

The thought occurred to me that maybe I really was Frederick Llewellyn Hovey Willis, that his life was my real life, and this school day was his dream about the future.

All I could think about was being done with the school day so I could go back to my cabin in the woods. If it really was identical to Henry David Thoreau's cabin in my dream, then I now knew something about it that I hadn't known before: there was a trapdoor in the floor. The cabin had a cellar. Henry David Thoreau hadn't let me go down into his. What was in there? Did it hold a clue to the meaning of the painting of the haunted camping trip that hangs on the wall?

It wasn't until fifth-period English class that I snapped to attention. We were finished talking about Louisa May Alcott's classic novel *Little Women* and moving on to an essay called "Nature" by the American philosopher Ralph Waldo Emerson. My teacher, Mrs. Dean, wanted to set the stage for Emerson by talking about the Transcendentalist Movement. For the first time all year—in fact, for the first time I could ever remember at school—I was rapt.

Mrs. Dean's presentation went like this:

This is Louisa May Alcott:

https://en.wikipedia.org/wiki/Louisa_May_Alcott

She grew up in the middle of an unusual confluence of great minds who came to be known as the Transcendentalists. Transcendentalism was the first American-made philosophy. It was born in Concord, Massachusetts, in the middle of the nineteenth century. A new and powerful way of seeing life, it spread far and wide. It is still inspiring people around the world today.

The three brilliant men who anchored the movement formed a triangle around Louisa May: her father, Amos Bronson Alcott; her teacher, Henry David Thoreau; and her neighbor, Ralph Waldo Emerson. What united these men was their deep conviction that society is a negative influence on the human spirit. Human beings are not born blank slates, needing to be shaped by parents, church, school, and government. Human beings are divine sparks that must find the courage to shape themselves—and not just themselves, but their whole reality.

Alcott, Thoreau, and Emerson rejected the Christian religion of their day, which insisted that God is a being *beyond us* (transcendent) to be worshipped and obeyed. Instead, they perceived God within nature and concluded that human beings, as part of nature, are part of God. We can *reach beyond* (transcend) ordinary experience to achieve divine consciousness.

Critics of Alcott, Thoreau, and Emerson labeled them "Transcendentalists" as an insult, thinking that such a big, ugly word would convince people that these philosophers were completely misguided. But it didn't. The name stuck, and Transcendentalism became an American heirloom.

This is Amos Bronson Alcott:

www.britannica.com/biography/Bronson-Alcott

Alcott was a utopian. He believed that human beings could work together to create peace-loving communities. He loved peace so much that he pioneered veganism, refusing to consume meat, dairy, eggs, or any other animal products. He fathered four girls and raised them without using punishment. He established a farming commune, which invited its members to escape the economic rat race so that they could cultivate their own spiritual perfection. He ran a series of schools in which the children, whom he believed to be innately endowed with pure intuition, taught the teachers. Alcott's utopian experiments didn't last. Were they failures, or were they just too far ahead of their time?

This is Henry David Thoreau:

Thoreau was an individualist. He went out to the woods alone to live in close communion with nature. He built a simple house for the modern-day equivalent of something less than a thousand dollars. In it were three chairs: one for solitude, two for friendship, and three for society. He discovered that the less you have, the happier you are. The addictive desire for more and more possessions causes greed, which causes exploitation, sometimes on a grand scale. Meditating on the shores of Walden Pond, reading Hindu and Buddhist works, Thoreau found "higher laws" in his own conscience that prompted him to protest immoral human laws. Years later, Martin Luther King, Jr., and Mahatma Gandhi cited Thoreau as their model for civil disobedience.

This is Ralph Waldo Emerson:

www.loa.org/writers/263-ralph-waldo-emerson

Emerson was a scholar. He toured America and Europe, speaking eloquently on topics designed to help ordinary people lead better lives. Though raised in poverty, Emerson inherited money as a young man, which enabled him to bankroll the Transcendentalist Movement. He bought the land for Thoreau's cabin and repeatedly saved the Alcott family from bankruptcy. He launched a magazine, *The Dial*, for Transcendentalists to publish their ideas. He provided personal and professional support for many struggling young geniuses of his day, such as the early feminist Margaret Fuller, the free-verse poet Walt Whitman, and the novelist Nathaniel Hawthorn, who wrote *The Scarlett Letter.*

Transcendentalism was driven by a Romantic love of nature. *Romantic*, in this sense, refers to Romanticism, a European intellectual movement emphasizing the wild yet ennobling power of the natural world. In the United States, Romanticism was visually captured by the landscape artists of the Hudson River School. This painting of the Grand Canyon typifies the Hudson River School:

The Grand Canyon of the Yellowstone, Thomas Moran, 1872 (https://fr.wikipedia.org/wiki/Fichier:Thomas_Moran_-_Grand_Canyon_of_the_Yellowstone.jpg)

Notice the two tiny people in the foreground against the breathtaking enormity of the canyon. There was never a more dangerous beauty than the American wilderness. Members of the Hudson River School fearlessly ventured out into unexplored regions of the country in order to show how valuable that wilderness was. In the nineteenth century, the Grand Canyon was widely regarded as a hellish wasteland, to be avoided or, better yet, vanquished by civilization. Thomas Moran's painting of the Grand Canyon, however, helped to convince Americans that it is a sublime treasure, to be protected and preserved—

Mrs. Dean's lecture cut off here due to an outbreak of laughter from the back of the classroom. Jake Bristol had evidently fallen asleep and started snoring. This set off the kids sitting around him. Snickering cascaded across the room.

The disruption angered Mrs. Dean. She shouted at the class, provoking an avalanche of further misbehavior. The students had reached the limit of their attention span.

I looked around in despair. Didn't anyone else want to hear about Transcendentalism? Only one face looked as dismayed as I felt: Ivy's.

Mrs. Dean ordered the students to take out their books and start reading the Emerson essay in silence.

Ivy crossed her arms over her chest and glared at me, as though this turn of events had been my fault. Something about the stubborn look in her eyes made me think of Louisa May Alcott defying Henry David Thoreau on the shores of Walden Pond.

When the bell rang a few minutes later, Mrs. Dean was still steaming. "Your homework assignment is to write a paraphrase of Emerson's essay—*due tomorrow.*"

I caught Ivy's arm when we got off the bus that afternoon. She was startled.

"Hey," I ventured.

"Hey," she echoed noncommittally.

"You want to work on the paraphrase for Mrs. Dean together?" I asked this because Mrs. Dean always urged us to do writing assignments in groups. It made the assignment half as hard if you could find someone you could trust to do half of the work.

"Okay."

I followed her to her house. We worked on her back porch. The following is what we wrote.

CHAPTER
ELEVEN

Ralph Waldo Emerson's "Nature"
by TJ O'Shay and Ivy Smith

To get to the truth about life, you have to escape society and find solitude. That means being truly alone.

You can't just shut yourself up in your room. Even aside from electronics, your room holds books, pictures, furniture, and a million other things from other people. To find solitude, go out into the night, and look at the stars. The rays that shine down from those distant worlds will cut you off from all reminders of society.

Imagine what it would be like if the sky was always cloudy and we never saw the stars. Then we would have no sense of the sublime. Human cities are great, but they're nothing compared to the stars.

Imagine what it would be like if the stars appeared only one night every thousand years. People would be totally blown away—they would never stop talking about it.

The stars are messengers of beauty. They smile at us every night, while scolding us for taking them for granted.

Anything in nature can awe you as much as the stars—if you're open to it. Nature is always a mystery. We never master her. She is not a toy to be played with and then tossed aside.

Suppose you could look back and identify the best hour of your entire life. The flowers, the animals, the mountains—they reflect the wisdom of that hour. Nature contains the simplicity of childhood, the complexity of death, and every profound moment in between.

This is a poetic approach to nature. It is based on an impression of wholeness. While a woodcutter is interested in a stick of timber, a poet is interested in the entire tree.

The gorgeous landscape I walked through this morning is made up of some twenty or thirty farms. Miller owns this field, Locke that, and Manning the woodland beyond. But the horizon is something no human can divide or own. It represents the unity behind the multiplicity of natural objects.

We are all born nature lovers. While the sun shines into the eye of the adult, it shines into both the eye and the heart of the child. The flowers, the animals, the mountains—they are like daily food to the young. What happens to us when we grow up? Society pulls our inward and outward senses apart.

But you can reconnect with your inborn love of nature. Learn to let its wild delight run through you, vanquishing your sorrows. Nature says, "You are my creature. Your griefs are small and irrelevant. You will be glad with me." Not the sun nor the summer alone, but every hour and season can be refreshing in its own way. Each change causes a different state of mind, from breathless noon to grimmest midnight. Nature can also be funny or sad. In all its different flavors, it is like a delicious drink.

In fact, nature recently gave me an inexplicable, transcendental experience. Crossing a bare common, in snow puddles, at twilight, under a cloudy sky, without thinking about any special good fortune, I enjoyed a perfect exhilaration. I became happy *to the brink of fear*.

In the woods, too, I cast off my years, like a snake shedding his skin, and I am a child again. Under the festive forest canopy, a party is under way—the kind of party you would never get tired of in a thousand years. In the woods, I return to optimism. There I feel that nothing terrible can happen to me in life.

Standing on the bare ground, a breeze lifting my head toward infinite space, I lose myself. I am nothing. I see everything. I become a transparent eyeball. The currents of the Universal Being circulate through me. I am part or particle of God.

At times like this, the name of the nearest friend sounds foreign and accidental. Every social relation—brother, neighbor, fellow citizen—is a trifle and a disturbance. I am the lover of uncontained and immortal beauty. In the wilderness, I find something more intimate than in streets or villages. In the tranquil landscape, and especially in the distant line of the horizon, I behold my own nature.

A hidden relationship connects human beings to the non-human beings of the fields and woods. As I set out on a trail, tall grasses nod to me, and I to them. As I hurry home through a storm, the boughs of a tree wave to me. The messages of nature take me by surprise. But the power to produce these messages does not reside in nature. It resides in us—or rather, it resides in our harmony with nature.

Nature always wears the colors of the spirit. The same scene that yesterday breathed perfume and glittered with frolicking nymphs is spread with melancholy today. When you are suffering, you will see sadness in your own campfire. When your friend dies, you will see contempt in the clouds.

Looking for the truth about life, following the invisible steps of thought, we come to inquire: What is nature? What is *our* nature? Are the two really one?

That Universal Being we experience in rare moments gives us the answer. It is not wisdom, or love, or beauty, or power, but all in one, and each entirely. The Universal Being is an all-pervasive spirit that creates the world. It does not act upon us from without. It comes from within ourselves. This spirit produces nature through us in the same way that a tree produces new branches and leaves through the pores of the old.

Human beings rest upon God just as a plant rests upon the Earth. We are nourished by unfailing fountains and draw on inexhaustible power. Who can set limits to the possibilities of humankind? Once we inhale the upper air, we learn that we have access to the entire mind of the Creator. Each of us is a finite realization of the creator.

As a poet, I say: Nature is not fixed but fluid. Spirit alters, molds, and makes it. Without spirit, nature is immobile, brute. With spirit, nature can be volatile or obedient. Every spirit builds itself a house, and beyond its house a world, and beyond its world a heaven.

Pour your spirit out! A revolution will unfold. Pure ideas will transform reality. If you can make the disagreeable element in swine, spiders, and snakes vanish, then you can make the disagreeable element in madhouses, jails, and enemies vanish, too. The sun will dry up the filth, and the wind will blow it away.

Just as the advance of summer melts the snowbanks and greens the Earth, the advance of spirit enchants its path with ornaments. It will multiply beautiful faces, warm hearts, wise discourse, and heroic acts until evil is no longer seen. Boldly forging this path, we will feel more wonder than the blind man who is gradually restored to sight.

All of nature exists for you. Build, therefore, your world!

CHAPTER
TWELVE

Emerson's "Nature" essay is pretty heavy reading. Writing the paraphrase was exhausting. Ivy and I worked through dinner. Her mom made pizza for us. We didn't finish until almost nine o'clock.

Needless to say, I didn't get a chance to go to the cabin. It was raining anyway. My mission to check out the trapdoor would have to wait until the next day.

After we finished the paraphrase, Ivy and I sat with our legs dangling off the porch, watching the rain and eating the fudgsicles we'd promised ourselves as a reward for getting the work done.

"So Emerson was a nature lover," I mused. "I've run into plenty of them before. And I can kind of relate. Like, sometimes when I'm out fishing on the pond, I listen to the crickets and look at the sky reflected in the water, and, well, it feels pretty cool."

Ivy nodded. "But Emerson wasn't just an ordinary nature lover. He's saying something much weirder than that in this essay. He's saying that God is our own spirit *creating the world*."

"That part seems totally whack." I licked a drip of chocolate from my thumb. "I mean, when I'm out on the pond, I don't feel like I'm *creating* the crickets and the sky and the fish. If I could create fish, I'd create a lot more big ones!"

"Right." Ivy frowned. "So what was Emerson talking about?"

I went home that night both excited and nervous about returning to the nineteenth century. It took me a long time to fall asleep. When I finally slept, I slept dreamlessly, as far as I could remember. My mom had to drag me out of bed the next morning.

At school the next day, Ivy and I turned in our paraphrase to Mrs. Dean. Ivy asked Mrs. Dean what Emerson meant when he said that "we create reality." Mrs. Dean said that all she expected the class to understand was the nature-loving part of the essay. If we wanted to understand the rest, we would have to read about it on our own. She gave us the following article, which we read on the bus on the way home from school that afternoon.

Ralph Waldo Emerson's Transparent Eyeball
by Sharon Kaye
Professor of Philosophy
John Carroll University

Ralph Waldo Emerson's essay "Nature" astonished the world. It starts with a bold question: What is the truth about life? And it ends with a shocking answer:

We are all God. This view, known as pantheism, is not as outlandish as it sounds. In fact, pantheism is a promising solution to a dire philosophical problem.

The problem is: How do human beings know anything about the world?

Most people do not see this as a problem at all. We make observations. Over time, they add up to knowledge. Right?

The empiricist philosophy of the eighteenth century formalized this commonsense view. Empiricism is scientific: the five senses of sight, hearing, smell, taste, and touch make human beings instruments for recording the facts.

But empiricism also makes the mind passive, which leads to skepticism. If human beings are instruments for measuring the world, then who will test us to be sure we are accurate? An instrument cannot test itself. Or if it did, it would also have to test the test, and test *that* test too, and so on to infinity. In the end, we would have to get outside of our own minds to see whether our measurements matched reality, but we cannot. So empiricism, despite its commonsense confidence, makes it impossible to know anything for certain.

The German philosopher Immanuel Kant, alarmed by this problem, famously developed an alternative to empiricism called "transcendental idealism."

Transcendental idealism begins with the thesis that the human mind is not passive but active. On its own, the world is nothing but a giant blob. We have to impose human categories onto this blob in order to experience it. This can be hard to imagine, but picturing cookie cutters on cookie dough is a start.

Without the mind, there are no distinct colors or shapes. The mind creates colors and shapes by experiencing reality through the concept of space. Likewise, without the mind, there is no discernible sequence of events. The mind creates a sequence of events by experiencing reality through the concept of time. Space and time are human categories through which we create our reality. They are the cookie cutters that we use to make our cookies.

Kant's transcendental idealism makes it sound as though we should be able to make the blob around us into whatever we want, but the categories we use to create the world are categories of *reason*. While I can *imagine* a pink elephant popping into the room, I can't make it real. Logic limits us to experiencing what necessarily follows from what we have already experienced.

True knowledge is possible, for Kant, because everything that exists is already a thought inside our heads before it becomes real outside our heads. To understand the inside is to understand the outside— hence the name *transcendental idealism*. Ideas cross (*trans*) over from the mind into the world.

That is as far as Kant went. He did not think that our ability to structure the blob made us God.

The American Transcendentalists who read Kant, however, took his solution one step further. If the human mind creates *facts* (such as the fact that there is a brown table but no pink elephant in the room), then why can't it create *values* (such as the beauty of a flower or the goodness of an action)?

If we can impose the categories of space and time on the world, then we can impose the categories of good and evil. Just as we cannot make a pink elephant out of a table, we cannot make a bad act good, or vice versa. Just as we have to obey logic in creating facts, we have to obey conscience in creating values.

But in creating both facts and values, we create all reality. So, for the Transcendentalists, we are God.

Needless to say, this thesis has many radical implications. Most importantly, it implies that each of us is an equal authority on the truth. Individual reason is the ultimate arbiter of what is real. No church, no sacred text, not even Jesus himself can override personal intuition. That is Ralph Waldo Emerson's carefully considered and clearly stated view.

Just in case anyone thought he was kidding, Emerson followed up his "Nature" essay with a series of other essays that traced out these implications. When he delivered one as the commencement address for Harvard, it got him banned from that illustrious institution for three years.

Emerson was surprised by the hostility he provoked. Disliking conflict, he stopped advertising what his deep love of nature had taught him. But the transparent eyeball had already been unleashed. Emerson wrote: "Standing on the bare ground,—my head bathed by the blithe air, and uplifted into infinite space,—all mean egotism vanishes. I become a transparent eye-ball. I am nothing. I see all. The currents of the Universal Being circulate through me; I am part or particle of God."

This is pantheism. It is a provocative possibility.

CHAPTER
THIRTEEN

"I still say it's whack," I complained as Ivy and I got off the bus.

"I actually think it makes a lot of sense," Ivy countered.

I huffed in surprise. "Ivy, if each of us was making reality, our realities would be totally different from each other. Just like when two people make cookies, they make different kinds."

"Not if we have the same dough to work with and the same cookie cutters," Ivy objected. "I mean there will be some variation, but that's true of peoples' realities, right? Your reality isn't identical to mine. It's similar, but it's not the same because we think a little differently."

I scowled in disbelief that Ivy was falling for Transcendentalism.

"Consider an ant," Ivy proposed. "What is an ant's reality like? Do you think it sees colors and shapes like we do? Do you think it remembers the past and anticipates the future the way we do?"

I thought about it.

"No way," Ivy pressed. "An ant just sees a blob of unidentifiable shapes and colors, and its life is a blur. Its brain is too small to separate things into categories. It doesn't know me from you, from my dog, from a tree, from a rock. For an ant, the whole world is divided into just two categories: food and not-food."

I had once put on glasses that were made to simulate what the world looks like to a bug, and Ivy was pretty much right. The compound lenses made everything a confusing jumble.

But I shrugged, not wanting to concede the argument. "That doesn't mean the world really *is* just a blob. Bugs' eyes are inaccurate instruments. Our eyes are accurate."

"Oh really?" Ivy raised an eyebrow at me. "What if there's a species of aliens out there with eyes that are even better than ours? They have more categories in their brains for what they see. So their reality will be different."

I had thought about the alien possibility before—aliens that saw a whole different set of colors or that were aware of objects we aren't aware of.

I took a different tack. "Even if it were true that the world was a blob that we have to structure, that still doesn't make us God. I mean, you still need someone to create the blob in the first place."

Ivy thought about that. "What if the blob was just always there?"

"That's impossible," I protested, my voice cracking. "Everything comes from something. Everything has a beginning."

Ivy's mouth curled into an incredulous grin. "Does that apply to God, too?"

"Of course not," I shot back. "God always existed. That's what they mean when they say that God is eternal."

"Well, if God can be eternal, then so can the blob," Ivy insisted. "I don't get the difference—"

Just then, a wolf whistle pierced the air. It was coming from a group of girls who had gotten off the bus together—Ivy's friends.

"Come on, lover-girl," Samantha taunted Ivy.

"Planning a big date?" Natalie echoed.

Ivy shot me an angry look, as if this turn of events was somehow my fault, and then ran across the street to join them.

Well, good, I thought. *I need to get on with my mission.*

I trotted to my house, dumped my backpack in my room, grabbed a flashlight, and headed out to the woods. If the cellar was empty, I would move my bombs there for safer keeping.

The cabin was the same as always, with no sign of use since I had been there last. I shone my flashlight along the floorboards in the middle of the room. There it was: a square seam with a two-inch slot in the middle of one end—the trapdoor.

I was nervous. What could be down there? I wasn't sure I wanted to know. What if there was a dead body down there? What if it was the body of the person who had written in the notebook in the drawer? That would explain why the cabin seemed so suddenly deserted.

I dropped to my knees and inhaled with my nostrils wide. The air was still tangy and sweet. Surely a dead body would cause a stench.

Steeling myself, I slid four fingers of one hand into the slot and gave a yank. It didn't budge.

I stood and straddled the square seam. Slipping two fingers of each hand into the slot, I gave another yank. Still no movement. Frustrating.

My eyes searched the cabin for something to wedge into the slot like a lever. Nothing. So I went back outside to look around for a stick. While kicking around in the undergrowth, I checked on my bombs. They were still there, just where I'd left them.

At last I found a few thin sticks that looked strong enough to function as a lever for me. Though the first one was a little too thick, the second one fit the slot just right. When I pressed all my weight against it, I thought I felt some movement. I wedged it in at an angle, took a step back, and then jumped on it as hard as I could.

The stick broke, and I nearly broke my ankle, but it was worth it: the trapdoor popped up. Though it fell back down, it was still ajar. I grabbed it and threw it open before it could slide back into place.

A black hole.

A new odor wafted into the cabin—not death, exactly, or at least not recent death. It was the ancient death of musty earth that never sees the sun. I shone my flashlight in.

This cabin's cellar was just like Thoreau's. The floor was about seven feet down. The trunk of a medium-sized tree served as a ladder. I dropped to my knees and swept my flashlight across each mud wall in turn. The space looked to be about six feet by six feet.

Against the first wall was a crude, wooden shelf holding several jars, rusty canisters, and burlap sacks. Against the second was a loose pile of moldy-looking blankets. Against the third was a battered wooden trunk. Against the fourth was.... Was that a little door?

It sure looked like a little door, about three feet square. A closet?

Well, there was no stopping now. I was just going to have to go down there. I needed to know what was in the trunk and behind the door.

I shimmied down the pole and then stood still, listening, with my feet on solid mud. So this is what it would be like to be in a grave someday. I could hear faint skittering coming from the shelf. I scanned it with my flashlight. Surely nothing lived down here. My heart started to race.

At the bottom of the shelf, my flashlight fell on two tiny white hands with sharp claws. Before I could stop myself, I yelped out loud. Behind the claws was a gaping mouth in a face without eyes. It was a mole. With a blind, whiskered sniff, it turned and disappeared through a small hole under the shelf.

I took a deep breath and moved to the trunk. Though a lock hung on its tattered latch, it was broken. I slipped it out and opened the lid.

Inside the trunk were two musty old army uniforms—one blue and one gray. The blue one had tarnished brass buttons in a double line down the front. The gray one had one line of buttons and faded gold trim. Each had a matching hat. The gray hat had a broad brim all the way around, like a flattened cowboy hat. The blue hat was more like a baseball cap with a stubby front brim.

Underneath the uniforms was a cache of weapons: some kind of rifle with a nasty knife-like point attached to the tip, a short curved sword, two revolvers, and three knives. All looked beat up, as though they were well used.

Underneath the weapons was a loose stack of papers. Up until then, I had only been digging gently down into the layers. In order to get to the papers, I would need to lift some of the uniform pieces and weapons out of the trunk and set them on the floor.

I was already shifting from foot to foot with the sensation of needing to go to the bathroom. The cellar was a dark and unpleasant space. The entire floor was smaller than a king-sized bed. I wanted out. On the other hand, the papers would surely solve the mystery of the cabin once and for all.

Just as I picked up the first hat, I heard the familiar creak of the door of the cabin above me. I froze. *Caught at last!*

Who would it be? The cabin's owner, no doubt, come to bust me for trespassing. How much did he know? Could I claim that this was my first time? Did he know about the bombs?

Having seen the army uniforms, and realizing they must be from the Civil War, I felt sure it would be old Mr. Smith. But he rode in a wheelchair most of the time. Was he really mobile enough to reach this remote location in the woods?

I didn't have time to think. I pushed the lid of the trunk down and dove for the closet. Crouching, I unlatched the door and pulled it open.

Another black hole.

It was not a closet. It was a tunnel. The beam of my flashlight was gobbled up by the mud walls. About five feet ahead, the tunnel seemed to turn left.

Hearing footsteps on the floor above my head, I killed my flashlight, ducked into the hole, and puled the door shut behind me.

It must lead out, I reasoned, trying to quiet my breathing. *Just crawl. This is your escape hatch, you idiot.*

But no matter how hard I tried, I could not make myself crawl into that darkness. A series of hideous deaths flashed before my eyes: suffocation, getting buried alive, falling into a well, getting bitten by poisonous spiders or rattlesnakes.

I stayed put, crouching with my hand on the door handle, willing myself to wait. Maybe it was just a passing trespasser, like me, who would see that the cabin was empty and leave.

Crap! I left the trapdoor open!

The moment I had that thought, I heard something. *Someone sliding down the pole? Or is it just my imagina—*

The door yanked open.

C H A P T E R
F O U R T E E N

Aaahhhh!

We screamed in each other's faces. With my hand still on the door handle, I was pulled so forcefully from the tunnel that I slammed right into my pursuer, knocking us both to the ground. Scrambling for our flashlights, we blinded each other until we could see who was who.

"What are *you* doing here?" we demanded at the same time.

It was Ivy. She was sprawled on her back, propped up on one elbow.

"Oh man." I rose and offered her a hand. "You scared me so bad."

"*I* scared *you*?" Ivy harrumphed. "You're the one who's not supposed to be here."

"And you are?"

"Of course." Ivy brushed her hair from her face. "It's my granddad's cabin."

It took me a moment to process this information. "You mean Mr. Smith?"

A distant memory flashed through my mind of Ivy, when she was little, walking down the road, holding Mr. Smith's hand. He would walk her to the bus stop every day for afternoon kindergarten. That was some ten years ago.

Ivy nodded and started climbing up the tree trunk out of the cellar.

Now that she was there, however, the oversized grave seemed much less intimidating. I didn't want to leave. I wanted to know what those papers were all about.

"Have you seen the stuff in the trunk?" I asked.

"Come on," she called. "I'll tell you about it."

And so she did, all the way back to her house for another fudgsicle on the back porch. This is what she said:

Her granddad's health has been deteriorating for years. Last winter he was diagnosed with cancer. Treatment has been unsuccessful, and he's not expected to live much longer. When meeting with Ivy's mother and a lawyer concerning his will, Mr. Smith talked about a valuable painting he wished to bequeath to Ivy. He claimed that the painting was hidden in a cabin that belonged to his granddaddy. Ivy and her mom were surprised to learn about the cabin. With some difficulty, they located it and discovered the poster of *The Philosophers' Camp* by William James Stillman in the trunk in the cellar. But they found no sign of any valuable painting. So Ivy's mom gently informed her father that he must have been thinking of the poster. That made Mr. Smith angry. It pushed him further into the despondent silence that had been growing between them for years.

At this point, Ivy is the only family member that Mr. Smith will speak to. He told her that he bought the *Philosophers' Camp* poster because it goes with the painting he hid. The painting shows what the philosophers in the poster were looking at.

So Ivy called the Concord Free Library, which owns the original *Philosophers' Camp* painting. They informed her that the painting depicts Ralph Waldo Emerson and his friends on their famous camping trip to the Adirondacks just before the Civil War. The museum staff had no information about another painting that was supposed to go with *The Philosophers' Camp*. They also had no information about what the philosophers were supposed to be looking at.

When Ivy asked her granddad what the missing painting looked like, he clammed up.

"He got this glazed look in his eye," Ivy told me. "It was as if he could see the painting as clear as day right in front of him. He said it was beautiful and dreadful at the same time. He kept the canvas rolled up rather than displayed in a frame because he could hardly stand to look at it. When he tried to describe it, he choked up and couldn't speak. His sadness turned to anger. He said it was just as well that it was gone, since I was too young to know about such things. Then he shouted at me to leave."

"Huh." I stood looking out into the swampy woods behind Ivy's house, trying to picture such a painting. "What about the papers in the trunk? There has to be a clue in there."

Ivy got out her phone and swiped to her photos. "The lawyer says we shouldn't move anything until after Granddad, you know, passes. But I took a picture of each sheet. There are twenty-something of them. It's just a bunch of records about armies and battles during the Civil War."

I studied the faded ink on the yellowed paper in the photos. "Hmm. So you're the one who left the notebook in the drawer?"

She nodded. "I put the *Philosophers' Camp* poster up on the wall so I could study it. Then I read for clues in the book in the drawer—*Walden; or, Life in the Woods*, by Henry David Thoreau."

I didn't think the book would be of much help. "Where does the tunnel go?"

"It comes out on the other side of the hill." She pantomimed the cabin set against the hill and showed how the tunnel curved left and then out.

"That's weird." I jumped off the porch and wandered meditatively into the backyard.

Ivy followed me, brainstorming explanations. "Maybe dirt cellars were supposed to be ventilated. Or maybe it was more than that. Granddad's cabin seems to be modeled on the one Thoreau built. In *Walden*, Thoreau writes that he dug his cellar at the side of a hill where a woodchuck had formerly dug his burrow. Critter burrows always have two holes, you know, in case of danger."

"Danger?" I echoed. "Do you think someone was after your granddad's granddad?"

Ivy picked a long blade of grass from the edge of the yard to nibble on. "Why else would you build a cabin for yourself out in the woods?"

I scooped up a cricket to examine. "Thoreau did it because he loved nature. He just wanted to be out there away from society—to feel the 'Universal Being' flowing through him or whatever."

Ivy squinted skeptically. "Maybe."

I frowned. "What are you getting at?"

"Well, Thoreau was one of Emerson's philosopher friends," Ivy pointed out. "So he might have known about whatever it was that was out there in the woods, which they were all looking at in the painting."

I recalled how defensive Thoreau seemed about his cellar in my dream. He clearly did not want me down there. Did his cellar have a trunk, a pile of blankets, and a tunnel as well?

"I know what you're thinking." Ivy was studying my face intently. "We have to go back into the dream to find out."

C H A P T E R
F I F T E E N

"What?!" I exclaimed. I suddenly felt as though I was looking at Ivy through the wrong end of a telescope. I blinked hard, trying to make the world normal again.

Ivy smiled slyly. "Come on. You had to know Louisa May is me."

I looked around to see if I could spot a hidden camera filming my reaction to this insane conversation. There was no camera.

"Is this some kind of trick?" I sputtered. "I never told you that I dreamed about Louisa May Alcott."

"Right. You didn't tell me," said Ivy. "I was there."

"That's impossible."

"Well, I would have thought so, too—if it hadn't actually happened."

"I must have told you I dreamed about Louisa May Alcott," I muttered, almost to myself. "Characters in dreams are often modeled on real people in your life."

Ivy grabbed my shoulders and shook me as she spoke. "Except I had the same dream! And you were in it, as Louisa May's friend, Llew Willis."

I spun away from her. "Ha ha!" I spat.

"TJ, this is serious. We have to talk about it." Ivy was scowling at me.

I turned to get a lock on her face, and I could see that she was serious—absolutely serious. So naturally I started to laugh—a bit hysterically.

"Okay, joke over." I suddenly felt absolutely serious myself. "Now it's time to tell me what's going on."

Ivy stuck her hand in her jacket pocket and pulled out the dreamcatcher that I had seen in the copy of *Walden* at the cabin.

"I think it's all because of this." She handed it to me. "Did you see it when you found the book in the drawer?"

"Yes," I confessed. "It fell out. I put it back."

"And that night you had the dream."

Was it that night? Yes, it was. I nodded.

"Well, I've had the dream four times now," she explained. "It's always after I've been to the cabin to look for clues in the book. At first, I figured it made sense that I would dream about Thoreau after reading his book. But the dream was so much more vivid than normal. And the first three times it was always the same. Llew wasn't there. As Louisa May Alcott, I would go with my sister Anna to Thoreau's cabin for tutoring. But the last time, the dream was different. Llew was there. We went to the cabin together and then to Spiderland afterward."

"At the end, you accidentally made a reference to the painting," I recalled, "and got us booted out of the dream."

Ivy nodded, relieved that I was finally ready to believe her.

"Look what's engraved on the bookmark," Ivy urged. The hoop of the dreamcatcher was attached through a string of beads to a silver handle, which was designed to serve as the page marker so that the hoop could dangle free from the pages. An elaborate engraving of the sun and moon decorated one side of the silver handle. That was the only side I had noticed. The other side held words:

> Our truest life is when we are in dreams awake.
> — Henry David Thoreau

"Whoa." That was all I could manage.

Ivy glanced nervously over her shoulder and shoved the dreamcatcher back in her pocket. If her mother caught her with her granddad's stuff, she would no doubt be in trouble.

"Let's walk the loop," she suggested, referring to the path that led from her backyard down around the neighborhood pond.

I followed her mutely, trying to breathe deep and pretend that it was normal for people to have waking dreams together.

"Did you know," she ventured, "that Henry David Thoreau wrote 2,800 pages in longhand about the Native Americans?"

"No." I wondered how many volumes that would be if it were typed.

"Those pages are called his 'Indian Notebooks.' Only excerpts have been published. Thoreau traveled to Minnesota to spend time with the Ojibwe tribe, which invented the dreamcatcher. This dreamcatcher I have in my pocket, if it was his, could be a real Ojibwe dreamcatcher."

That idea sent a shiver down my spine.

"Thoreau died of tuberculosis at the age of forty-four in the middle of the Civil War," Ivy continued. "Do you know what his last word was?"

I didn't answer.

"Indian."

"So let me get this straight." I ducked under a low-hanging branch on the path. "You're trying to say that this dreamcatcher was Thoreau's and that it's somehow putting us into the same dream."

Ivy shrugged. "It's easier to believe *that* than to believe that the dreamcatcher is actually taking us back to the nineteenth century. I suppose syncing dreams is a lot like syncing electronic devices."

"But how? And why?"

Ivy reached into her pocket for the dreamcatcher to have another look at it as we walked. I held out my hand, and she handed it to me.

"No one knows how dreamcatchers work," Ivy conceded. "But I read that they often take on the obsessions of their owners. This dreamcatcher seems bent on recovering the lost painting. It wants history to know what the philosophers were looking at out there in the woods."

We fell into silence as we passed the old boathouse. A memory of the previous year's fireworks display coasted through my mind. I wondered whether Mr. Smith would be well enough to put on a show this year. I wondered how Ivy would feel about me blowing up the boathouse.

"Will you come back to the dream and help me find my granddad's painting?" she asked me.

"Well," I sighed, handing the dreamcatcher back to her, "if this thing works by physical contact, then I may not have much choice."

C H A P T E R
S I X T E E N

That night I returned to the dream. It was strange. I can remember having the same dream more than once, or at least having a series of similar dreams. But I don't remember ever returning to a dream to continue it—until now.

The dream picked up on the following day, Saturday. Louisa May Alcott, Bronson Alcott, and I, as Llew Willis, were walking up Lexington Road in Concord, Massachusetts, to Ralph Waldo Emerson's big, square, white house for the Saturday symposium. Louisa May carried a bouquet of wildflowers, Mr. Alcott carried an armful of books he had borrowed from Emerson, and I carried a pot of Mrs. Alcott's apple dumplings to share.

I caught Louisa May's eye, and we gave each other the slightest wink to confirm that we knew who the other was. Before parting that night in real life, we had agreed not to do anything out of character so that we wouldn't get booted out of the dream.

We were a little late for the symposium. Several people were already occupying the genteel furniture in the front parlor of the Emerson home. They were introduced to us as the biologist Louis Agassiz, the novelist Nathaniel Hawthorne, the poet Henry Wadsworth Longfellow, and the journalist Margaret Fuller. Two artists, who were hailed as Stillman and Ring, came in even later than us.

When everyone found seats and the small talk quieted down, Emerson stood in front of the piano. He was tall and thin with straight, dark, side-parted hair, an aquiline nose, and an aristocratic brow. He was wearing a suit with a hand-tied black bow, and he was holding what looked like some handwritten notes.

He cleared his throat and addressed us in a deep voice.

Thank you for coming, my friends. I wanted to speak to you this evening about the concept of self-reliance.

When is the last time you read something truly original? Have you ever?

The other day I received in the mail some verses written by an eminent painter. [Here Emerson winked in the direction of Stillman.] These verses were so original that I've forgotten what they were about! [Laughter all around the room] Seriously, though, what impressed me was the originality itself. And that's what got me thinking about self-reliance.

Original work inspires us to be original. This is more valuable than anything else about the work. To believe in your own thoughts, to believe that what is true for you in your private heart is true for all people—*that* is genius.

We praise Moses, Plato, and Milton, not for knowing books, traditions, or what other men thought but for what *they* thought. Genius is a gleam of light that flashes across the mind. We should learn to detect it and welcome it. Instead, we are taught to dismiss it without notice simply because it is *ours*.

Great works of art are majestic. They teach us to uphold our own spontaneous impressions, even when everyone cries out against us. Tomorrow, a stranger might say precisely what you thought but lacked the courage to say. Then you'll be in the awkward position of taking your opinion from someone else.

Be a nonconformist. Don't try to be good. Explore what goodness is. In the end, nothing is sacred but the integrity of your own mind. Be true to yourself, and the world will listen.

When I was young, a friend of mine tried to teach me religion. I said, "What do I care about sacred traditions? I live by my own impulses."

My friend said, "What if these 'impulses' of yours are not from above but from below?"

I said, "They don't seem to be. But if I am the devil's child, then let me live by the devil!" [Surprised murmuring and guffawing around the room]

No law can be sacred to me but that of my nature. "Good" and "bad" are just names that can be applied to anything. I am ashamed to think how easily we capitulate to names, to large societies, and to dead institutions. Every decent and well-spoken individual affects and sways me more than is right. I ought to stand up and speak the rude truth in all ways.

Hatred and vanity often wear the coat of charity. Suppose an angry bigot takes up the cause of abolition. He comes to me with the latest news about the slave trade in Barbados. Why should I not say to him, "Go love your children and your employees. Be good-natured and modest. Show grace to those around you rather than ambition for black folk a thousand miles away. Your love afar is spite at home!" Saying this would be harsh, but truth is handsomer than false love. Your goodness must have some edge to it or else it isn't really goodness. Hatred is the only medicine for a love that complains and whines.

When my genius calls me, I shun father and mother and wife and brother. They accuse me of following a whim. A whim! I should paint that word above my front door. I hope that my genius is somewhat better than a whim, but we cannot spend our lives trying to explain ourselves. Don't expect me to explain why I seek or exclude certain company.

A good man told me today of my obligation to help the poor. [Here Emerson winked in Bronson Alcott's direction.] Are they *my* poor? I grudge every dollar I give to people who are not *my* people. For my people I will go to jail, if need be. But I am ashamed of giving to miscellaneous popular charities—the education of fools, the building of useless meeting-houses, alms to drunkards, and the thousands of Relief Societies.

People do what is called a "good action" much as they would pay a fine. Their charity is an apology for their living in the world. Just as invalids and the insane pay high rent, they pay high penance.

I do not wish to atone for guilt but to *live*. My life exists for its own sake, not as a spectacle. I prefer to be genuine, even if that is unglamorous. I know that, for myself, it makes no difference whether I do or don't do those actions that are deemed excellent. Few as my gifts may be, I actually *am*. I do not need my fellows to testify on my behalf.

What I must do is all that concerns me, not what the people think. This rule is hard because you will always find those who think they know what your duty is better than you do. It's easy while living in the world to live by the world's opinion. It's easy while living in solitude to live by your own opinion. But great people are those who, while living in the world, maintain the perfect independence of solitude.

CHAPTER
SEVENTEEN

The audience applauded Emerson, and a lively discussion ensued. I followed some of it, but mostly I found my mind sinking into my own thoughts.

I'd never heard any adult, especially not any respected adult, saying such outrageous things. Mrs. Dean had said that Emerson was one of the most influential philosophers of the nineteenth century. I mean, he was really famous and really important in shaping American culture. And look at what he said! It's not what you would expect. It's not the same old crap about being good and obeying the rules—not at all. It's the opposite. Emerson was basically saying that if anyone tries to tell you what to do, you just tell them to go pound sand.

Now *that* is a philosophy I could relate to. I think it's because I feel like I've been out of sync for so long. As long as I can remember, I've found myself questioning stuff that other people just go along with. Why do I have to sit still and be quiet and do as I'm told? What makes my parents and my teachers and everybody else think they know what's best for me? They don't. Only *I* know what's best for me. When they try to tell me my business, it makes me want to blow stuff up.

This year I set out on a mission to be bad. I don't know anymore if I really want to be *bad*. I just don't want to be good *according to their definition of it*. I'm offended by them trying to impose their definition on me. It makes me feel like something less than human—like a dog or a monkey to be trained. Sure, I'm still a kid, but I'm *human*, and every human being has a conscience of his or her own. We have the right to figure out for ourselves what to call "good."

Knowing that I didn't want to be good according to *their* definition, I figured that my only option was to be bad. I didn't realize that there was another possibility. And it's a possibility recommended by the great Ralph Waldo Emerson: exploring your own definition of good. I wonder what that would be like. I wonder if I could go for that.

Here's what kills me: people try to make me feel bad for being out of sync, as though *I'm* the one standing in the way of progress, when really it's *them*. They're standing in the way of *genius*. You have to be original to be a genius. People who go along with the crowd will never do anything valuable at all.

Just as I was finishing that thought, I noticed Louisa May looking at me expectantly, as if she had said something.

"Huh?" I said, broken from my reverie.

"I *said*," she huffed, "are you going to come and make a plate for yourself?"

"Oh." I realized that everyone was getting up and moving toward the dining room. "Yeah, sure."

We filed past the elegant oak buffet table and helped ourselves to an abundance of dishes: baked beans, brown bread, crab cakes, salt cod, and squash pie, among other things, including "quahogs," which, I found out, are clams. They're not bad. A little squishy, but not bad.

Louisa May, who was careful not to take any of the food that was made from an animal, and I sat and ate on the steps at the bottom of the staircase leading to the second floor of the house. While we munched, we listened in on the conversation wafting around us.

Alcott: I think, if you really listened to your conscience, Emerson, it would tell you that abolition is *not* an empty charity. It is a vital moral duty!

Emerson: I'm listening as hard as I can, Bronson.

Hawthorne: Oh, Emerson, don't listen to all that talk. Abolition is a sham. It's so easy for Northerners to sit around tsk-tsking about slavery when their wallet doesn't depend on it. If the Southern states give up slavery, they'll go bankrupt. Bankrupt, I tell you!

Longfellow: Which is to say that Southern plantation owners are getting rich from the suffering of others.

Hawthorn: Suffering! I'll tell you who's suffering: the white assembly-line workers in the North, that's who. It would be better to be a slave than to work at the Thoreau family pencil factory for $7 per week. The machinery is dangerous, and if you're injured, guess what: you're fired! At least on the plantation, slaves know they've always got a home.

Alcott: I'm sure the Thoreau family treats its workers better than that.

Hawthorne: Then they'll be pushed out of business soon because I guarantee you there's another clever gent out there who's willing to hire desperate women and children for even less.

Agassiz: That's appalling. My research proves that the white race is superior to the black race. Their race, not ours, should be making pencils.

Fuller: Ugh! We're all the same race, you idiot—the *human* race. Neither women nor children nor black people should be working in subhuman conditions. Obviously, slavery must be abolished, *and* factories must be improved.

[Applause from Mr. Alcott; then an awkward silence]

Stillman: Speaking of Thoreau, where is he? I thought he was coming tonight. I wanted to propose a camping trip.

Emerson: [Laughs] For the lot of us?

Stillman: Absolutely. You philosophers are always going on about finding your true self in the solitude of nature. Well, how often do you get out there? Walking to the train station doesn't count!

[Everyone laughs.]

Stillman: Seriously. I want to paint you out there. Transcendentalist painting. I want to show my young apprentice Ring how it's done.

Agassiz: Splendid! We can collect specimens and hunt.

Longfellow: If Emerson is bringing a gun, I'm definitely *not* coming!

[Everyone laughs.]

Emerson: Oh, come on! Not one of you can shoot any better than I can. In fact, that would be a great benefit of this camping trip: we could brush up on our woodsman skills.

[Everyone begins to chatter about the idea of a camping trip.]

Louisa May and I observed the repartee in silence from behind the banister on the stairs. Just one other member of the group was equally silent: Ring. Hardly older than Louisa May and I, he studied the group with big, haunted eyes.

Catching me staring at him, he got up and approached, opening his mouth as if to say something. But before any words could come out, there was a commotion at the front door. As everyone stopped chattering and turned to look, Emerson's wife Lidian swept into the parlor with a new guest. He was out of breath and sweating, hat in hand, his bright red hair plastered to his forehead.

Emerson rose from his chair, his brow knit. "Who are you, and what the devil's the matter?"

"My name is Daniel Duncan Smith" the man panted. "I'm here to tell you that Henry David Thoreau is in jail!"

CHAPTER
EIGHTEEN

"Sit down, man," Emerson ordered, striding to the dining room to pour a glass of water for his impromptu guest. As Smith sank onto the couch, everyone gathered around to hear his story.

"Are you from these parts?" Margaret Fuller asked.

"I was born and raised in Still River," Smith explained, "but Thoreau and I went to Harvard University together."

"Oh, wait a minute," said Bronson Alcott. "I remember the Smith family from when we lived in Still River. There were twin boys."

"Yes, that's us." Smith cringed, as though ashamed to speak of his family. "My brother Darvin and I are the twins."

Alcott nodded, trying to piece the memory together in his mind. It was clearly not a pleasant memory for him, but he was trying to be charitable. "I seem to recall that your family is...a bit...controversial."

Smith swallowed hard. "Most of my family is from Louisiana, and so yes, they are vocal supporters of slavery."

The air in the room began vibrating with tension. I realized at that moment that the Smith family was the family

I was supposed to be staying with for the summer—the one my grandmother had sent me to, which Mrs. Alcott had saved me from.

"For crying out loud!" Stillman protested. "Forget about politics for one minute, people, so he can tell us what happened to Thoreau."

Smith took a long drink of water as the room quieted down. "Well, I arrived in Concord this morning—"

"From where?" Margaret demanded.

"Red River, Louisiana." Smith set his glass on an end table with an unsteady hand. "A few years ago, my brother and I inherited our uncle's plantation. I've been living down there, working as a Unitarian minister, but I returned this week to visit family. I figured I would stop and see Thoreau on my way to Still River. I went to his family's house on Texas Street, and they told me where to find his cabin in the woods."

"You didn't go out there, did you?" Hawthorne scoffed.

"Yes," Smith brightened. "Thoreau and I spent the afternoon together. He took me out on the pond in his rowboat. It was nice. When I told him about some trouble I've been having with the Unitarian Church, he invited me to come to this symposium with him tonight. He said you used to be a Unitarian minister, Mr. Emerson."

"That's true," Emerson conceded. "I resigned because I did not agree with some of their doctrines."

Smith nodded sympathetically. "Thoreau said it would be good for me to talk to you about why I'm thinking of resigning."

"So how did Thoreau get arrested?" Stillman burst out.

"Well," Smith continued, "we walked into town a little early because Thoreau had to stop at Jonas's Bootery to get his shoe fixed. On our way there, the sheriff stopped us—"

"Sam Staples?" Bronson Alcott interrupted. "Let me guess: he arrested Thoreau for tax evasion."

Smith cocked his head. "How did you know?"

"His predecessor got me on the same charge a few years ago," Alcott confessed. "But he never threw me in jail."

"Seriously!" Emerson erupted. "Why won't you men pay your taxes?" He got up and paced to the kitchen and back.

Alcott crossed his arms stubbornly on his chest. "Because we are protesting the State."

Emerson sighed. "The State is a poor, good cow. It means to be friendly. Do not begrudge it some hay. Ninety percent of what you pay, the State will spend on things you deem good. Only ten percent is spent on mischief."

"I'd say slavery is more than ten percent mischief," Alcott shot back.

Emerson harrumphed. "Tax evasion is mean and skulking and in bad taste."

"Gentlemen!" Margaret shouted. "Stop it! We need to figure out what to do."

"Well, we can't leave him in jail," Emerson grumbled. He reached in his jacket pocket and pulled out a fistful of cash. "I'll simply have to bail him out." He started counting bills onto the table. "It can't be more than ten dollars."

"Be careful coming to the rescue for degenerates, Emerson," Hawthorne warned, "lest your reputation sink into the sewer along with them."

"I'd say it's time for a cigar," Agassiz remarked.

Hawthorne agreed wholeheartedly. The two men convinced Emerson to have a smoke on the back porch with them.

"I'll take the money to the sheriff," Alcott announced, rising to collect the money.

"No, Bronson," Margaret warned. "He's liable to throw *you* in, too."

"Ring and I will go," Stillman offered.

"But you're strangers here in Concord," Margaret argued. "As is Smith. It will have to be me."

"People would say it is no job for a woman," Stillman objected, "to go to the jail alone after dark."

"Well, then, people would be wrong," Margaret spat.

"Llew and I will go with you," said Louisa May, jumping up and scooping the money into her handbag.

CHAPTER
NINETEEN

And so it was decided. Margaret Fuller, Louisa May Alcott, and I slogged through the muddy streets of Concord to the jail. By the time we arrived, the sheriff had already left for the night. The guard invited us to return in the morning.

"That's not going to work." Margaret planted her fists on her hips in annoyance. "I'm off to Boston at dawn to conduct some Conversations."

"Conversations?" I asked.

"They're classes I run for women," she explained. "If they won't let us into the university, then we'll just have to educate ourselves, right?"

"Um, right," I agreed.

"My classes aren't much," she conceded. "But the way I see it, if you give enough women a taste of the education they're missing, pretty soon they'll be clamoring for more, and then they'll break down the walls barring them from the universities."

"Absolutely!" Louisa May cheered. "I would like to go to Harvard just like Emerson and Thoreau."

"Good for you." Margaret clapped Louisa May on the back. "I had to fight just to get Harvard to let me into its library for research on my first book. The Harvard library had never let a woman in before me! I'm afraid it might be more than a hundred years before any woman is allowed to earn a degree from that old boys' club. In the meantime, come to Boston, and sit in on my Conversations."

"Maybe I will," Louisa May grinned.

"But as for today, I happen to know where the sheriff lives. Why don't we go there now and see if we can't get this disagreeable business of Thoreau's taken care of?"

So we slogged even farther to Sam Staples's home.

Mrs. Staples answered the door looking cranky. "Who are you, and why are you knockin' on my door on a Saturday night?"

Without giving our names, Margaret told Mrs. Staples that we had brought the tax money to spring Henry David Thoreau out of jail.

Pursing her lips in annoyance, the sheriff's wife disappeared into the house. When at last she returned, she was even crankier. "Sam's just taken his boots off, and he says he ain't goin' out again tonight. Leave six dollars, and he'll spring Thoreau in the mornin'."

Margaret and Louisa May looked at each other dubiously. The sheriff's wife rolled her eyes with impatience. At last Louisa May shrugged and handed over the money.

"Listen, you two," Margaret said to Louisa May and me as we walked away. "I want you to show up at the jail tomorrow to make sure that Sam Staples lets Thoreau out like his wife says he will. There's something fishy about this whole thing."

Louisa May snapped to attention. "What do you mean?"

"Well, think about it," Margaret mused. "Neither Alcott nor Thoreau has paid his taxes for years. And I know several other abolitionists in Concord who haven't either. Why Thoreau, and why now?"

"You think the sheriff had other reasons for locking up Thoreau?" I pressed.

Margaret nodded. "It would definitely be worth looking into."

"Do you think Thoreau is up to something illegal?" Louisa May asked.

Margaret narrowed her eyes. "Let's just say I don't believe him when he says he went out to the woods to live with the squirrels."

"But he doesn't say that," Louisa May corrected. "He says he went out to the woods 'to live deliberately.'"

"Right," Margaret granted. "And what does that really mean?"

Louisa May looked to me for an answer, but I didn't have one. A meditative silence fell over us. We dropped Margaret off at her younger sister Lennie's house, where she had been staying on and off for the past year. Lennie had two small children and a wayward husband. She needed all the help she could get.

"Despite being the nephew and namesake of a great Unitarian minister, Lennie's husband is turning out to be a bit of a disappointment," Margaret groused.

"Can you please explain to me what's up with all the Unitarians around here?" I asked Louisa May as we headed back to her house.

"All I know is that the Unitarians broke off from the Christian Church over the issue of the Trinity. They believe in God the father but not Jesus the son or the Holy Ghost— one *united* god, hence 'Unitarianism.' Emerson started his career as a Unitarian minister, but he went too far for them when he said that God is not a Father in heaven but a spirit in nature and in us all."

"Do you think that's why Smith is thinking of resigning?"

"Why don't you ask him yourself?" Louisa May pointed to Emerson's front porch, where Emerson and Smith sat on the steps talking. When they saw us passing, they met us in the street to hear our news. They were none too pleased to learn that Thoreau was stuck in jail for the night.

"In that case, you can stay at my house tonight," Emerson told Smith. Then he turned to Louisa May. "It's late, and your father has already gone home, so we'll say goodnight."

I caught Smith's attention as he turned back to the house. "Just one question."

"Yes?"

"Why are you thinking about leaving the Unitarian Church?"

Smith glanced at Emerson as though they had just been discussing that issue. "In the South, the Unitarian Church is supporting slavery. In the North, it isn't."

"Whose side are you on?" Louisa May asked.

Smith was still looking at Emerson. "I guess that's the big question, isn't it?" He did not elaborate but simply turned and shuffled into Emerson's house.

The next morning, Louisa May and I set out bright and early to the Concord jail to make sure that Thoreau was released, just as Margaret had advised. As we approached, we saw two men standing out front. Angry words were mounting between them. It was Thoreau and a large, burly man with a silver star on the lapel of his coat.

Thoreau: Sheriff, you can't throw me out of jail!

Sheriff: I got nothin' to keep you on. Yer taxes is paid.

Thoreau: But I did not authorize anyone to pay my taxes!

Sheriff: Believe me, I would keep you if I could—not because of the taxes but because of the other stuff.

Thoreau: What other stuff?

Sheriff: [Looks around; sees us coming] You know just what I am talking about, Henry David. It's a dangerous business, and someone's gonna get hurt.

Thoreau: This is—

Sheriff: Enough! Now git before I send a posse to seize your property.

Thoreau: —outrageous!

"Hello, Mr. Thoreau!" Louisa May called, waving brightly.

Thoreau turned toward us. The sheriff took advantage of the opportunity to return to the jail.

Thoreau was limp and speechless. His arms hung uselessly at his sides.

Suddenly, a pair of leather shoes came flying toward us through the open jail window. They landed in a muddy puddle on the dirt road with a splash.

"What's going on?" I asked. Having seen how angry Thoreau was about his taxes being paid for him, I thought it wise to pretend that we had no part in it.

Thoreau cleared his throat with all the dignity he could muster. Louisa May hastily collected his muddy shoes and handed them over to him. Meanwhile, a tall man in a shiny black suit and top hat had walked up. It was Emerson. Emerson and Thoreau stared at each other without speaking for a long moment.

"Henry David," Emerson pronounced at last. Though no longer a Unitarian minister, he had a way of coming across as a high priest. "Why were you in there?"

"Waldo," Thoreau mocked. "Why am I out here? Why are *you* out here instead of in there?"

Emerson blinked several times, as though cold water had just been thrown in his face. "I am on my way to Boston," he replied, "to give a lecture on 'The Poet,' in which I shall argue that words and deeds are different modes of the same divine energy."

"How nice," Thoreau intoned without enthusiasm.

Just then a horse-drawn wagon rattled down the road, drawing our attention.

"There goes the Miller family," Thoreau remarked. "I bet they're on their way to Concord's annual huckleberry party, which happens to be this morning, as I recall. Would you kids like to join me?"

So we did. It turned out that a huckleberry party is when a bunch of people get together to pick huckleberries. There were about thirty of us. We rode the Miller wagon out to a hill full of low, scrubby bushes that were heavy with huckleberries. Huckleberries look just like blueberries but taste terrible.

"Ugh," I complained as I spat out my first taste. "Why are we picking these things?"

"You bake them into pies, city boy," Thoreau replied.

"Oh." I couldn't imagine it would be worth it.

But for Thoreau, it was worth it just to be back in the wilderness. He returned to his jovial self, boxing with the children and "finding" huckleberries in their ears. No other members of the party had yet heard about his incarceration, so we didn't discuss it.

During the course of two hours, our party filled dozens of baskets, until our hands were purple and our backs were sore from bending. Fortunately, some of the women had brought honey sandwiches, dill pickles, and carrots to share. We had to send someone with a bucket to the river for fresh water to drink.

Thoreau, Louisa May, and I donated all our berries to a member of the party named Joe Polis. Joe was a Native American man who had married a white woman named Lydia Maria Child. She went by Maria (pronounced Ma-RYE-a). They had a daughter, "Little Bear," who was spending the week with her grandmother. But they were planning to make a big batch of huckleberry pies for a charity event at the church. Maria invited us to come and help them the following day.

"Me no like pie," Joe confided to us with a wink. "Some things we no tell our wives."

Thoreau and Joe clearly had come to the party for each other's company. Thoreau told Joe about a method he had devised to measure the depth of Walden Pond. According to legend, the pond was bottomless. Thoreau determined it to be 102 feet deep.

"I fathomed it with a cod-line and a stone weighing about a pound and a half," he explained. "I could tell accurately when the stone left the bottom by having to pull so much harder before the water got underneath to help me."

Joe was amused with Thoreau's interest in putting numbers on nature. Joe knew that the pond was deep enough for trout, which was all he needed to know.

When we dropped Thoreau off at his cabin later, he asked us to wait while he ducked inside to retrieve an unsealed envelope addressed in his handwriting to Ralph Waldo Emerson. "Would you please drop this off at Emerson's house when you get back to town?" he requested, handing the envelope to Louisa May. He looked exhausted, like a scraggly brown bear ready for a long afternoon nap.

Louisa May accepted the envelope, but we did not go straight back to town. We walked to Crosby Pond instead to visit Spiderland, where we read the contents of the envelope. We figured Thoreau would have sealed it if he didn't want us to. The following is what we read.

CHAPTER TWENTY

In case of my untimely imprisonment or death, I, Henry David Thoreau, hereby authorize immediate publication of the following unfinished manuscript.

Civil Disobedience
by Henry David Thoreau

In my view, the best government is the one that governs the least. Or, better yet, the best government is the one that does not govern at all.

To be practical, I will not demand the immediate abolition of the American government, but I will demand its immediate improvement. Let every American say what kind of government he or she would respect, and that will be one step toward obtaining it.

Why does the majority rule in America? Not because it is most likely to achieve justice but because it is physically strongest. Majority rule cannot achieve justice because right and wrong cannot be established by vote.

How are right and wrong established? By conscience.

We are human beings first and citizens second. My only true obligation is to do what I think is right. Law has never made me more just. In fact, law has made me *unjust*, for I too have been swept up in patriotic fervor.

Have you ever watched a parade of soldiers? Did your heart pound with the drums and take flight with the flutes?

Right now, amidst a fanfare of rousing music, American soldiers are marching off to Mexico to expand the slave states to the southwest. These soldiers march against common sense and conscience. If they were still human, they would know that they are involved in a damnable business.

So what have these soldiers become? Cogs in the machine.

Every machine has some friction. If injustice is a small kink in the machine, then let it go. Either the kink will wear smooth, or the machine will wear out. If the injustice has a spring, a pulley, or a crank to support itself, then consider the pros and cons of a remedy. But if the machine makes *you* the agent of injustice, then hesitate no longer: let your life be a counter-friction to stop the machine.

How should we regard the American government today? I answer that we cannot without disgrace be associated with it. We cannot obey a government that is the slave's government also. We have to disobey it.

In other words: *Break the law.*

I know this for sure: if one thousand, if one hundred, if ten men whom I could name—if ten honest men only—nay, if one *honest* man, ceasing to hold slaves, were to stop cooperating with the State and be locked up in jail, it would be the abolition of slavery in America.

Under a government that imprisons anyone unjustly, the right place for any just man is in jail. It is there that the fugitive slave and the Mexican prisoner and the Native American come to plead the wrongs against them. That separate ground is where the State places those who are not with her but against her.

You may think that your influence would be lost there, that your voice would not strike the ear of the State, but truth is stronger than error. Besides, you can combat injustice more eloquently and effectively when you have experienced a little of it yourself.

Suppose a thousand men refused to pay their taxes this year. That would not be as bloody a measure as it would be to pay them, for paying those taxes enables the State to shed innocent blood. Refusing to cooperate is the definition of a peaceful revolution, if any such is possible.

But suppose refusing to cooperate does result in bloodshed. It is still the less violent alternative, for a sort of blood is shed when conscience is wounded. Through this wound your humanity and your immortality flow out, and you bleed an everlasting death. I see this blood flowing now.

Of course, the American government has provided other paths for seeking reform, but these paths take too much time! (The State will make sure of it.) Before you see any results, your life will be gone. I have other affairs to attend to. I came into this world, not chiefly to make it a good place to live in but to live in it honestly.

America was founded as a refuge of liberty, yet a sixth of our population are slaves. It is not too soon for honest people to rebel.

Who are the worst opponents of reform? Not the multitude of Southerners but the multitude of Northerners who are more interested in commerce and agriculture than they are in humanity. They are not prepared to do justice to the slave. I quarrel not with far-off foes but with those who, near at home, cooperate with those far away—the enablers. Without them, the far-off foes would be harmless.

Thousands of Northerners are, in theory, opposed to slavery and the war in Mexico, yet they do nothing to put an end to them. They sit with their hands in their pockets, saying they don't know what to do. They hesitate, and sometimes even petition, but they have no effect. They wait, eager for others to remedy the evil so that they will no longer have to regret it. At most, they vote.

But voting is cheap. It is a sort of game, like checkers, with a moral tinge to it. I cast my vote as I think right, but I am not vitally committed to its victory; I'm willing to leave it to the majority. On the contrary, as a player in the voting game, I am actually approving whatever the majority votes—even if it is against my own vote and my own conscience.

A wise man will not gamble with morality like that. There is little virtue in the action of the masses. When the majority shall at last vote for the abolition of slavery, it will be because there is little slavery left to be abolished.

To be just, government must have the consent of all of the governed. The American government does not have the consent of conscientious Americans. Therefore, the American government is not just.

This does not surprise me much, and I shall devote the least possible thought to it. Thankfully, I live few of the many moments of my life under the dark shadow of the State. If your mind is free and your imagination strong, unwise rulers cannot fatally interrupt you.

The progress from absolute monarchy to limited monarchy, and from limited monarchy to democracy, is progress toward respect for the individual. But is democracy the last improvement possible? Or is it possible to take a step further? There will never be a truly free and enlightened State until the State comes to recognize the individual as a higher, independent power from which all its own power and authority are derived.

I please myself by imagining a State that can afford to do justice to all human beings. Or how about a State that leaves people alone as long as they behave as decent neighbors? This would prepare the way for that Stateless perfection that I also have imagined but have not yet seen anywhere.

CHAPTER
TWENTY-ONE

After Louisa May and I finished reading, we lay on the big rock that served as the main stage of the Spiderland Theater, tired from our morning of berry picking and puzzled by the essay.

"So," Louisa May ventured, "it seems as though the issue of slavery is blowing Thoreau and Emerson apart." She went to the stony ledge where she had hidden the unfinished "frenemy" poem that she had accidentally stolen from Thoreau. She read it out loud again:

> Surely, surely, thou wilt trust me
> When I say thou dost disgust me.
> O, I hate thee with a hate
> That would fain annihilate;
> Yet sometimes against my will,
> My dear E, I love thee still.
> If thou won't s

"I bet Thoreau was writing this about Emerson," she said.

I nodded. "After everything Emerson says about going out into nature, away from society, so that you can become a true original, you would think he would admire Thoreau. Thoreau is, like, the personification of Emerson's ideal."

"Well, they were best friends," Louisa May echoed. "After all, Thoreau built his cabin on Emerson's land. Without Emerson, Thoreau would probably be working in his family's pencil factory."

"But now they're split over paying taxes," I said, "which doesn't make much sense for pantheism. If they're both part of the same god or 'Ultimate Being,' then how can they disagree?"

Louisa May thought about it. "It's not always easy to tell the voice of conscience from other voices in your head."

"Remember when the sheriff said he wanted to keep Thoreau in jail, not for the taxes but for the 'other stuff'?" I asked. "Do you think he was referring to this essay? I mean, this essay basically calls for anarchy."

Louisa May shook her head. "The sheriff said he thought the 'other stuff' was going to get someone hurt. I think Thoreau is up to something else out here in the woods—something dangerous that he somehow justifies in his conscience, something the philosophers are going to find out about on their camping trip."

"Something that young painter Ring is going to paint," I added.

"Maybe Emerson already knows about it and is worried about it," Louisa May surmised. "But Thoreau seems like such a nice guy. Why would he be into dangerous stuff? Do you think he may be crazy?"

"It's possible," I granted. "I mean, his frenemy poem is dripping with hatred. It's threatening. And then he was basically begging the sheriff to throw him back in jail. It's hard to imagine *wanting* to be in jail."

"Is it?" Louisa May probed. "It seems like that's exactly what *you* want."

"Me?" I rolled over on my side to scowl at her.

"Well, no, not you, Llew," she amended. "I'm talking about a boy who reminds me of you, who I dreamed about. His name is TJ. He lives in the twenty-first century, where life is much easier than it is here in the nineteenth. For example, in TJ's world, you can get all kinds of berries that are much sweeter than huckleberries all year long. You just buy them at the store. You don't have to spend all morning picking them yourself. Despite such an easy life, TJ keeps getting into fights and getting suspended from school. Everyone says he's going to end up in jail someday."

"Oh, him." I didn't really want to talk about my "other self" while in this dream. Earlier, when we were walking through the majestic woods to Spiderland, I had caught myself thinking that I liked myself better as Llew.

"And what is TJ doing with all those boxes he had shipped to the old boathouse in his neighborhood?" Louisa May pressed.

"What boxes?" I bristled.

"Whatever he's up to," Louisa May insisted, "it can't be good."

"TJ's a Transcendentalist," I growled. "He doesn't obey other peoples' ideas of good and bad. He's making up his own definition. What he decides is good to him may not be good to anybody else."

"It seems to me that TJ doesn't understand Transcendentalism at all." Louisa May gathered up her skirts and started hopping from rock to rock across Mill Brook. "Listening to your conscience doesn't mean you get to do whatever you want, following any whim."

"It isn't a whim," I objected. "TJ is going to make a deliberate statement."

"There's that word again: *deliberate*," Louisa May complained. "Thoreau said he went to the woods to live deliberately. What does that mean?"

I followed Louisa May out onto the rocks in the brook. "The word *deliberate* means on purpose or carefully planned." My foot slipped into the brook. Icy water soaked my shoe.

"Great," Louisa May snapped. "So you can do whatever you want as long as you plan it carefully. I guess you and Thoreau really admire Caligula and Genghis Khan a lot then."

I narrowed my eyes at Louisa May, waiting for her to smirk at me the way Ivy does when she's with her posse of girls—the "you're not good enough" smirk. She didn't understand that this was no game to me. This was about life itself—whether it *means* anything or not. She was playing with fire—which can be dangerous. *Then we'll see if she can fight her own battles like she claims.*

Louisa May reached the other side of the brook, with me close on her heals. She jumped to shore and turned to face me. But she wasn't smirking.

Her head was cocked to the side, her cheeks bright pink with the effort of crossing the brook. She fixed a concentrated gaze on me, like she absolutely needed me to have an answer to her challenge—like it mattered to her as much as it did to me.

She looked so beautiful in that moment that I wanted her to stay that way forever. I stepped to shore—it wasn't quite a jump for me, being much taller. She didn't turn away or move at all.

I didn't have an answer to her challenge. All I had for her was a kiss. I reached for her face with both hands and tilted it up to mine.

CHAPTER
TWENTY-TWO

It was horrible to have to find a dead body. But it was especially horrible to have to find one right in the middle of that particular moment.

Louisa May scowled at me when I touched her face, unsure of what I was up to. When she figured it out, she jerked back, almost involuntarily, and turned to free herself. But then she stopped and looked back at me as though she decided that maybe she liked what was happening after all.

I wanted to kiss her then, but it was a little confusing because, in the end, it was still a dream. Would it count as a kiss in real life? If not, I decided right then and there that I was never going back to real life. In fact, why chance it? This dream could be my reality, our reality—Louisa May and me. Forget the twenty-first century.

But I hesitated too long.

"Hey," she said, looking past me. "I thought I saw something move behind you just now. Oh, look!"

I turned and saw what had caught her eye. It was a mangy dog, medium-sized with black and gray splotchy fur. My instinct was to push Louisa May behind me to protect her from an attack. I braced myself, looking around wildly for a stick or something I could use as a weapon. But the dog wasn't interested in us. It was feasting on bloody flesh—a recent kill. It detached a messy red bone with its teeth and trotted away, happy to avoid a confrontation and leave the rest to us.

I figured that the dead thing was a deer. I would not have gone any closer to find out. Unfortunately, it was lying on the sandy bank in full view. It was human—mauled beyond recognition, but human. Female, too, judging by the bits of bloody orange flowered material that were strewn about.

Louisa May's hands flew to her mouth to keep herself from retching.

I grabbed her arm. "We've got to go get help."

We dashed back across the brook and ran home. During one slow-down, while we caught our breath, Louisa May, eyes wide, said she thought she recognized the orange flowered material.

"Someone you know was wearing it?" I asked.

Louisa May strained to remember. "I feel like it may have been one of the garments Anna brought home for mending."

Back at the Alcott house, Louisa May's two little sisters were playing happily in the yard. We slipped past them into the kitchen, where we told Mrs. Alcott about the body. She sent us to the garden to tell Mr. Alcott. Mr. Alcott accompanied us to Emerson's house. The two men debated whether Sheriff Sam Staples could be trusted to handle the situation, given his recent treatment of Thoreau. It was decided that there was no other choice.

Louisa May and I had to accompany the men back to Mill Brook to show them where the body was. We rode a wagon drawn by a horse to get as close as the terrain allowed and then walked the remainder. The sheriff brought a crate to collect the body, but he vomited when he got close and then passed out. Emerson worked on reviving him while Mr. Alcott and the sheriff's deputy filled the crate with pieces of flesh, bone, and orange flowered material.

Meanwhile, Louisa May and I combed the perimeter for clues. Though it wasn't exactly a forensic investigation, we did turn up a clear trail of dog prints and human footprints coming from the southwest—the direction of Walden Pond. Louisa May picked up a scrap of the orange flowered material and shoved it in her skirt pocket for further reference.

The sheriff dropped the four of us off on our street before proceeding with his deputy and the body back to the police station.

"Well, I guess this puts an end to the philosophers' camping trip," Mr. Alcott told Emerson as we parted for our respective homes.

"Stillman and Ring are in Boston hunting down camping supplies and guides as we speak," Emerson objected. "I'd say it's too late to cancel the trip."

"Well, count me out, anyhow." Mr. Alcott was backing toward the house, holding his filthy hands away from his body, looking ill from the afternoon's adventure.

"But why?" Emerson demanded. "That dead woman's got nothing to do with us. She was probably one of the loggers' prostitutes."

"Thoreau said those loggers cleared out last week," Mr. Alcott countered.

"But there are all kinds of strangers like that coming through town in the summer. It could have been anyone. She got drunk, ran into the woods, got lost, and got attacked by a rabid dog or coyote."

"If there's a rabid dog or coyote out there, then that's reason enough to stay home," Mr. Alcott pronounced. "But I've never heard of a dog or coyote ripping someone to pieces like that."

Emerson planted his hands on his hips. "What are you suggesting?"

Mr. Alcott swallowed hard. "I'm not suggesting anything, friend. I just think we should consider the possibility that it was no coincidence that this ferocious attack occurred on the night that Thoreau was locked up in jail."

Everyone turned to see Mrs. Alcott coming out the front door of the house. When she saw the pallor on her husband's face, she bustled him inside. Emerson shrugged at me and Louisa May and then continued on down the road to his home. Louisa May ran after him to hand him the envelope from Thoreau, which she had almost forgotten in her skirt pocket. He accepted it with a pat on her shoulder.

While Mrs. Alcott was busy getting Mr. Alcott cleaned up and into bed for some rest, Louisa May and I snuck into the room that Anna shared with her two youngest sisters. (Louisa May had lobbied hard for a room of her own, which, though small as a closet, gave her the peace and quiet she needed to write.) On a chair in the corner of her sisters' room was a folded pile of garments that needed mending. Neighbors would drop them off, and Anna would get to them when she had time.

Louisa May pawed through the pile. "I feel like there was an orange flowered skirt in here."

If there had been such a skirt, it was gone now.

Louisa May's mouth dropped open in horror. "What if Anna was wearing it?"

"Hello!" It was Anna, home from her seamstress job.

Thank goodness!

We flew to the front door to greet her. Little Lizzie and Abby May came inside then, too. After an interval of small talk, Louisa May asked Anna about the scrap of orange flowered material she had recovered from the crime scene.

"Where did you get that?" Anna demanded. "I mended a skirt made from that same material for Thoreau's mother last week. It needed a new hem. Is this ripped from it?"

"Not sure." Louisa May tucked the scrap of material back in her pocket and changed the subject, without mentioning the dead woman.

No one spoke of the dead woman at dinner. Anna would be angry when she heard about it later, but Mr. Alcott, still gaunt, even after apple pudding, was in no condition to discuss it, nor would it be a good topic for the two youngest Alcott sisters to hear about.

The next morning, all of Concord was abuzz with two bits of delicious gossip: Henry David Thoreau's night in jail, and the dead woman in the woods. Sheriff Staples had posted some signs around town and in the stagecoaches passing through, asking for any information about a missing female of indeterminate age and appearance.

But no one knew who the dead woman was, much less what had killed her. No one was missing any wives or daughters or sisters—not in Concord, and not anywhere around Concord. It was as though the woman had popped into existence out of thin air.

And it was a problem because she needed to be buried, and soon. The sheriff said he would wait one more day before putting her in an unmarked grave in Sleepy Hollow Cemetery at the edge of town.

"Why do I have the strong suspicion that the philosophers are going to see whatever killed this woman when they go on their camping trip?" I asked Louisa May as we stood at the kitchen sink washing breakfast dishes.

"I have the same feeling," Louisa May confessed.

"Do you think the philosophers are in danger?" I pressed.

Louisa May nodded. "And I think it may be up to us to stop whoever or whatever it is from striking again."

CHAPTER
TWENTY-THREE

Louisa May and I resolved to go talk to Thoreau. On the one hand, being in jail gave him the perfect alibi for the crime, especially since he had been with Smith all afternoon. On the other hand, he could have killed the girl in the morning, before Smith arrived.

We needed to rule Thoreau out. We would inform him about the dead woman and observe his reaction. Being isolated in his cabin two miles outside of town, he wouldn't have heard about it. We would be able to tell whether he knew something, whether he was somehow responsible.

Neither of us was too happy about the mission, however. All I could think of was the crazed look in Thoreau's eyes when he was arguing in front of the jail with Sam Staples. He had seemed like a different person then. I didn't relish the prospect of confronting him about a serious crime out in the middle of the woods.

It came as a relief, therefore, when Anna, late for work, asked us to deliver some more mended garments to Thoreau's mother. Perhaps we could investigate Thoreau indirectly.

We set off across town toward Texas Street, about a mile and a half away, where the Thoreau family housed itself and its pencil factory. It was a sunny summer day. I took a deep breath as I fell into step with Louisa May, my mind wandering back to our almost-kiss by the brook. With all of the hysteria surrounding the dead woman, we hadn't spoken of it. I wanted to know how she felt.

I stole a casual glance at her out of the corner of my eye. She glanced at me and then looked away, apparently thinking about the same thing—and just as embarrassed about it.

"So, Mr. Willis," she sniffed in her most ladylike voice, "you were acting awfully strangely in Spiderland yesterday."

I shrugged noncommittally. "Things happen in the woods. Inexplicable things."

She didn't exactly smile, but on the other hand, she didn't frown either. I took that as a good sign. We walked in silence for a moment. It was everything I could do to keep from reaching for her hand. I wanted to touch her face, taste her mouth, and feel her body against mine.

"Transcendental things?" she asked.

I recalled the definition of *transcendental* from our last quiz in Mrs. Dean's class:

Transcendental: An experience, event, object, or idea that is extremely special and unusual and that cannot be understood in ordinary ways

I nodded definitively, not trusting my voice to speak without cracking.

"Well, then," she declared, "we shall have to go back to the woods again soon."

Before I could decide how to respond to that, an oxcart loaded full of squawking chickens in coops pulled onto the road in front of us. It was an interesting spectacle, complete with a lanky black dog patrolling the inmates—conveniently preempting further conversation about *us*. We followed the tottering vehicle almost all the way to the Thoreau family house.

I found out later that Thoreau had helped his father build the house, which had provided good training for building his cabin on Walden Pond. In the front room, Thoreau's mother ran a shop where you could buy pencils, as well as baked goods on Wednesdays. In the middle room, employees cut the wooden shafts for the pencils, sanded them, and inserted the graphite. In the back room, always locked, Thoreau's father worked on improving the secret graphite recipe that made the Thoreau family pencils the best pencils in the United States.

Young Henry David was actually responsible for a good deal of his family's success. Like other American pencil makers, Thoreau's father had been binding graphite powder together with wax. Those pencils were very brittle. Studying sturdier, European pencils, Thoreau determined that clay made a better binder. Clay could only be used, however, if the graphite powder was more finely ground. So Thoreau invented a new kind of graphite grinder that was tall enough to collect the finest graphite dust settling at the top. Although Thoreau's secret recipe paid for his college education at Harvard University, his heart wasn't in the pencil business, and he was happier living at Walden Pond.

Mrs. Thoreau was not in the shop when we arrived. Instead, a young woman with a long nose and auburn hair, who looked like she had to be Thoreau's sister, sat at a desk by the window with a freshly made pencil in her hand. She was drawing a sketch of a robin in the yard.

"Well, hello, Louisa May!" the young woman hailed, rising from her chair. "Who's your friend?"

"Hello!" Louisa May replied, awkwardly clueless about the young woman's name. "This is Llew Willis. He's boarding with us for the summer."

"Welcome to Concord." The young woman extended her hand for me to shake. "I'm Sophia Thoreau."

Louisa May presented Sophia with a burlap sack containing the garments that Anna had mended.

"Why, thank you." Sophia opened the sack and piled the garments on her desk. "I'm hopeless with mending. And mother is too busy taking care of poor Helen." Sophia glanced at me and realized that I wouldn't know who she was talking about. "Helen is my older sister."

"What happened to Helen?" Louisa May asked.

"Haven't you heard?" Sophia swallowed hard, determined not to get emotional. "She's come down with it—the same thing that killed grandfather. She's coughing up blood. Doc says it's consumption. I guess they're calling it tuberculosis now. I'm reading an article about it. Anyhow, we're doing everything we can for her. Father says it runs in the family."

"Tuberculosis? Hereditary?" I objected, ready to set her straight.

Louisa May elbowed me in the ribs to keep me from spouting anachronisms that would get us booted out of the dream. "They don't really know yet what causes it," she said to me.

"Right," confirmed Sophia, "even though it's the number-one killer in the country." She handed us her magazine and pointed to the article she had been reading. "They estimate that 400 Americans die of it *every day*."

"That's horrible," I replied, knowing that what she said was true. Tuberculosis is a highly contagious disease caused by bacteria that spread through the air when an infected person coughs or sneezes. "Is Helen here in the house?"

Sophia nodded. "Upstairs."

Louisa May and I locked eyes, feeling the urge to flee the germs that we knew must be near.

"Have *you* experienced any symptoms?" Louisa May asked Sophia.

Sophia shook her head. "But everyone else in the family has had it on and off for years. Doc says my brother John would have died of it if he hadn't died of tetanus instead."

"Really?" I was alarmed. Thoreau's vigorous outdoor life away from his infected family was probably the only thing keeping him alive.

"To be honest, I don't think it's hereditary either." Sophia lowered her voice. "This article talks about the vampire theory."

Louisa May's heavy eyebrows shot up. "Vampire theory?"

Sophia nodded. "There was a family in Rhode Island dying off one by one. Finally, they figured out that it was all because their grandfather had escaped from the grave and was feeding on their blood at night!"

Louisa May struggled to keep a straight face. "You think your grandfather is feeding on your family?"

Sophia folded her arms across her chest defensively. "My grandfather was an arrogant man. On his deathbed he cursed God and said he didn't deserve to die. I wear a silver cross to bed every night, and I'm the only one who hasn't shown any symptoms. How do you explain that?"

I frowned, wondering whether she was born with a stronger immune system. I knew I wouldn't be able to voice that explanation out loud.

"Henry David claims he doesn't believe in vampires." Sophia fingered her silver necklace. "But he admits that he's fighting all kinds of demons out there in the woods."

"Hmm." Though I didn't believe in vampires, I had dreamed about them. And this was, after all, a dream. "Has he ever been more specific about what demons he's fighting and *how* he's fighting them?"

Sofia shook her head and returned to her seat at the desk. She looked as though she wished she hadn't raised the issue.

"One more thing," Louisa May begged. "Anna wanted us to ask you about the orange flowered skirt she mended for you last week. She said she thought she might not have finished it, and you should check to see if it needs to be sent back."

"Orange flowered skirt?" Sophia screwed up her face for a moment, and then it dawned on her. "That was an old skirt of mine. The mended hem looked fine. But I decided it was really too small for me." She glanced toward the stairs and lowered her voice again. "Reverend Sewall is hosting a major charity event for the homeless at the Unitarian church this week, and his daughter Ellen is helping with a rummage sale. I gave it to her."

"Why are you whispering?" Louisa May whispered.

"Well," Sophia hedged, "mother doesn't really like it that I'm still friends with Ellen after her rejection of Henry David."

Sophia was surprised by the puzzlement on our faces.

"Don't you know?" she prompted. "I figured everyone knew. Henry David asked Ellen to marry him."

CHAPTER
TWENTY-FOUR

Next stop: the parish house of Concord's Unitarian church. It was easy enough to know where the church was from seeing its spire. It was the tallest building in town. In fact, we had passed by it on Lexington Road not long after we'd passed Emerson's house.

Louisa May was walking fast, alarmed. "What if Ellen Sewall saw that orange skirt in the pile and decided she liked it so well that she wanted to wear it herself?"

"Her family would have reported her missing by now," I countered. "Just because she rejected Thoreau's marriage proposal doesn't mean he would kill her."

Louisa May's expression was chiseled in stone. "The name *Ellen* starts with *E*."

My mind catapulted back to Thoreau's unfinished frenemy poem:

> Surely, surely, thou wilt trust me
> When I say thou dost disgust me.
> O, I hate thee with a hate
> That would fain annihilate;
> Yet sometimes against my will,
> My dear E, I love thee still.
> If thou won't s

Perhaps it wasn't about Emerson after all. Perhaps it was about Ellen Sewall. Did Thoreau hate her enough to lure her into the woods, kill her, and leave her body to be ripped to pieces by wild dogs?

Louisa May rapped hard on the door of the parish house. A pretty young woman with glossy black hair, a cleft chin, and ice-blue eyes answered the door.

"Ellen?" Louisa May ventured.

"Greetings, cousin!" Ellen cooed.

"Greetings!" Louisa May sighed with relief—both at guessing correctly and at finding Ellen alive. "This is Llew Willis. He's boarding with us for the summer. We wanted to ask you about your rummage sale."

Ellen smiled shyly, revealing crooked teeth. "Please come in."

As we followed Ellen into the foyer, she made polite inquiries about the Alcott family. Louisa May played along with the small talk as best she could but turned the conversation our way as soon as possible. "Anna mended one of Sophia's skirts, and she accidentally put it in the donation pile. We've come to retrieve it." Louisa May pulled the scrap of orange flowered material out of her pocket and held it up. "It's made from this material. Have you seen it?"

"I'm just sorting clothing donations now," Ellen said, touching the cloth without any sign of recognition. "They're on the dining room table."

We followed Ellen through a cluttered hallway to an even more cluttered dining room. Ellen had not gotten far with her sorting. There was a small mountain of clothing on the table. We set to work separating it into men's trousers, men's shirts, women's dresses, and children's clothes.

"I can't believe all the cotton in this pile, Ellen remarked, subtly noting that Louisa May and I wore muslin just like she did. "You would think the people of Concord would unite in banning cotton."

"You would think," Louisa May echoed.

I united a pair of socks. "I guess that's something you and Henry David have in common: your abolitionism."

Ellen blushed, no doubt having heard about Thoreau's recent stint in jail. "I suppose so, yes," she confessed. "But really it was more our love of nature that the four of us had in common."

I felt my forehead puckering. "The four of you?"

"Me, Henry David, his brother John, and my brother Eddy." Her eyes went soft, to the dreamy place where memories live. "The four of us were inseparable last summer. We hiked and fished and caught turtles and got terribly muddy—wonderfully, terribly muddy!"

Louisa May and I nodded sympathetically, remembering our own recent bout with the mud at Thoreau's cabin.

Ellen folded a pair of trousers, carefully smoothing out the wrinkles. "I believe that Henry David will be a famous writer someday. I *would* say a famous scientist, but he's a different kind of scientist—a kind of scientist that doesn't really exist yet."

"What do you mean?" I asked.

Ellen studied me, trying to decide whether or not she liked my prying interest. She wanted to like it, I could see, provided that she could trust me. I adopted the most innocent, unimposing face I could muster. It passed Ellen's test. Without a word, she dropped the garment she was folding and left the room, returning a moment later with a handful of papers. Louisa May and I stopped sorting and gave her our full attention to encourage her to go on. So she did.

"We were collecting turtles for Louis Agassiz—you know, the famous biologist. If we brought him samples, he would pay us for them because he wanted to study them. Well, we stopped bringing Agassiz turtles when we found out what he was doing with them: all kinds of dreadful experiments. Henry David studied the turtles too, but he would never hurt them. He included this excerpt from his journal in a letter to me:

> Consider the turtle. A whole summer—June, July, and August—is not too good nor too much to hatch a turtle in. Perchance you have worried yourself, despaired of the world, meditated the end of life, and all things seemed rushing to destruction, but nature has steadily and serenely advanced with a turtle's pace. The young turtle spends its infancy within its shell. It gets experience and learns the ways of the world through that wall. While it rests warily on the edge

of its hole, rash schemes are undertaken by men and fail. Has not the turtle also learned the true value of time? You go to India and back, and the turtle eggs in your field are still unhatched. French empires rise and fall, but the turtle is developed only so fast. What is a summer? Time for a turtle's eggs to hatch. So is the turtle developed, fitted to endure, for he outlives twenty French dynasties. One turtle knows several Napoleons. He has seen no wars, has had no cares, yet has not the great world existed for him as much as for you?

Ellen shuffled through her papers thoughtfully, a little sadly. "And then the loggers came through and destroyed the area where the turtles lived, so we stopped going there. The trees they chopped down were sold for cheap lumber and firewood. Henry David was furious. This is what he wrote."

A great part of our troubles originate from living in big houses. What right has my neighbor to burn ten cords of wood when I burn only one, thus robbing our half-naked town of this precious covering? Is he so much colder than I? It is expensive to maintain him in our midst. One man uses a little driftwood from the river (unmarketable!), and Nature rejoices in him. Another, Herod-like, requires ten cords of the best of young white oak or hickory, and he is commonly esteemed a virtuous man. Let men tread gently through nature! I shall burn stumps and worship the out-of-doors, while Christian vandals destroy the forest temples to build miles of meeting houses and horse sheds and feed their box stoves.

Louisa May frowned quizzically. "It seems as though Mr. Thoreau has an unusual reverence for nature. I guess that stems from his Transcendentalism. He believes that God is in nature—that all of nature is divine."

"Yes," Ellen sighed, and she put aside the papers and resumed sorting clothes. "My father says the Transcendentalists are heretics."

"Is your father the one who refused to let you marry Mr. Thoreau?" Louisa May prodded.

Ellen flinched. "Well, that's the official story anyhow."

"What's the true story?" I pressed.

Ellen's gaze swept from me to Louisa May and back again. Her eyes grew glossy with tears. She wanted to tell someone, and she found no reason to hold back. "Because I learned that the love poetry Henry David wrote was not for me but for my brother."

Louisa May and I exchanged surprised glances.

Ellen took a deep breath, her burden unloaded, and went back to sorting. "I assure you that Henry David's special affection is lost on Eddy."

"Eddy?!" Louisa May and I mouthed the name simultaneously. We were thinking the same thing: Eddy—another *E*.

"However," Ellen added, "Henry David is busy planning a camping trip to the wilderness of Maine at the end of August. Eddy plans on going with him. Joe Polis will be their guide."

CHAPTER
TWENTY-FIVE

We did not find the orange flowered skirt on the Sewalls' dining room table—as Louisa May and I knew we would not. Ellen announced, however, that her mother had already sorted an earlier pile of clothing and had taken it to the rummage sale, which was in full swing at the Unitarian church.

After helping Ellen carry our newly sorted piles to the church in wicker baskets, Louisa May and I hunted through the rummage sale's clothing table for the skirt. It wasn't there. Of course not. The skirt was in a crate in the sheriff's office, about to be buried with an unidentified body.

With veiled urgency, I asked the two old ladies working the rummage sale cash box whether they remembered the skirt and who had bought it. No luck. There had been several shifts of cash-box workers and a lot of customers since Friday, when the sale had begun. Anyone could have bought that skirt.

As we bade Ellen goodbye, Louisa May casually inquired about her brother Eddy's current whereabouts. Ellen said that he was staying with relatives for the summer in Scituate, Massachusetts—a day's journey from Concord by stagecoach.

"Even if Thoreau wrote the frenemy poem to Eddy," I remarked to Louisa May when we were back on Lexington Road, "the dead body wouldn't be Eddy. What would Eddy be doing in an orange flowered skirt?"

Louisa May shrugged. "If Thoreau is gay, then he and his friends may be into cross-dressing."

I thought about it. She had a point. Surely gender-bending activities were invented long before the twenty-first century.

Given that there was no feasible way to check up on Eddy, we headed for the big white house on Sudbury Road that belonged to Joe Polis. After all, his wife, Lydia Maria Child, had invited us to come there and help make huckleberry pies. If anyone knew what Thoreau was up to in the woods, it would be Joe Polis, who had been born and raised a traditional Native American.

Maria greeted us at the front door, remembering our names. She was petite, with high cheekbones and sunken eyes. Her hair, gathered at the nape of her neck in a bun, was already mostly gray. She had the beleaguered look of a woman who had endured a great deal of judgment due to her interracial marriage.

"I'm so glad you're here," she said as she beckoned us into her home. "Little Bear isn't back from her grandmother's yet, and I need all the help I can get. The bake sale will be tomorrow, when the remains of the rummage sale are given away. The proceeds will benefit an Indian orphanage."

Joe was out on errands. We stayed anyway in the hope that he might be home soon.

Following Maria to the kitchen, we embarked on an adventure in nineteenth-century pie-baking. Fortunately, Maria had already made the dough. It was divided into twelve fist-sized balls that were chilling in the ice box, which was literally a box containing ice.

First, Maria brought out three giant ceramic mixing bowls. Following her instructions, each of us measured huckleberries, sugar, and a handful of other ingredients into our respective bowls and stirred the mixture with wooden spoons.

Then Maria brought out two heavy rolling pins. "I believe I have a third one in the garret. You're tall," she said to me. "Would you help me get it?"

"Sure," I replied, wondering what the garret was. I felt as though I had heard the word recently, but I couldn't quite remember.

It turned out that the garret was an attic. I followed Maria upstairs to the second floor, where there was a trapdoor in the ceiling. Maria retrieved a chair from one of the bedrooms. Standing on it, I was able to push the trapdoor up and reach a wooden crate on the floor above.

"Just hand that down to me," Maria instructed.

I did, and she quickly found the third rolling pin under a pile of embroidered handkerchiefs.

By the time we returned to the kitchen, Louisa May had wiped down the table and had dusted it with flour. We rolled the dough balls out to fit into tin pans and then poured the huckleberry filling into the dough-lined pans. Each of us made four pies, for a total of twelve.

At one end of the kitchen was a brick oven. It looked like a two-foot shelf built into the wall. Maria had lit a roaring fire in it a few hours earlier, before we'd arrived. Now all we needed to do was sweep the glowing embers out through a hole at the back and clean the surface so that the pies wouldn't taste of ashes.

Dipping a mop in hot water, Maria scrubbed the steaming surface of the shelf, all the while singing a jingle I recognized.

> Over the river, and through the wood,
> To Grandmother's house we go;
> The horse knows the way to carry the sleigh
> Through the white and drifted snow. Oh!
> Over the river, and through the wood—
> Oh, how the wind does blow!
> It stings the toes and bites the nose
> As over the ground we go.

Louisa May grinned at Maria. "Did you make that up?"

"I did," Maria confessed. "And I was thinking of adding another verse." She began singing again.

> Over the river, and through the wood—
> When Grandmother sees us come,
> She'll say, "O, dear, the children are here,
> Bring a pie for everyone!"

When she was finished washing the oven, Maria tested its temperature by throwing a dash of flour in. Since the flour didn't burst into flame, she was satisfied that the oven was cool enough. When Louisa May tried to set one of the pies on the shelf, however, she nearly singed her eyebrows off. Maria chuckled and brought out a long, flat, wooden shovel. She used it to position the pies in four rows of three. Then she shut the oven doors and latched them tight.

"Well!" Louisa May exclaimed, wiping sweat from her brow, "let's hope someone invents better ovens soon!"

It was time to escape from the kitchen heat into the parlor. Maria brought out a pitcher of iced tea along with a platter of cheese, crackers, and tomatoes. Meanwhile, Louisa May and I collapsed on the sofa, exhausted.

That's when I caught sight of it. A dreamcatcher—just like the *Walden* bookmark, except as big as a hula hoop—was hanging on the wall.

"Oh my!" Louisa May erupted when she saw what I was looking at.

"Oh," Maria demurred. "Little Bear made that."

"Really?" Louisa May got up to examine the intricately woven silver threads. "It's beautiful."

Maria beamed. "Little Bear is learning traditional tribal religion from her grandmother, Nooko. When Little Bear was born, Nooko made a dreamcatcher to hang in her crib. Indians use dreamcatchers to protect children from bad dreams. Little Bear always loved her dreamcatcher. When she got older, she learned how to make different kinds, and she even did a research project on them. She has come to believe that dreamcatchers have the power to catch all kinds of evil spirits. She's currently making an even bigger dreamcatcher to hang in the woods."

My ears pricked up. "Why in the woods?"

Maria nibbled thoughtfully on a cracker as she prepared her explanation. "Little Bear is trying to catch the Wendigo, a forest monster that feeds on human flesh. As I understand it, the Wendigo started out as an ordinary human who broke the moral law against eating one's own kind. One taste, and he was hooked. The more flesh he eats, the taller he grows and the skinnier he becomes. The skinnier he becomes, the hungrier he gets. The hungrier he gets, the greedier he gets. The Wendigo is now huge and crazed for human flesh, haunting the woods for any opportunity to feed."

Maria broke off, reading the look of puzzled horror on our faces. "The story is allegorical." She shrugged defiantly. "A warning against greed."

"But Little Bear believes the Wendigo is real?" Louisa May probed.

"What *is* reality, Louisa May?" Maria demanded, reddening. "Indian religion includes many different kinds of spirits that are foreign to us. The Wendigo is just as real to Nooko as Jesus is to the good Christians of Concord. Little Bear has the right to follow the religion of her people."

I felt a shiver go down my spine as I wondered, once again, what the rules were for this dream. Could vampires and wendigoes exist in its reality?

Louisa May cocked her head sympathetically at Maria. "Will Little Bear eventually go to live with her tribe, do you think?"

"It looks like it," Maria sighed. "Her tribe recognizes the third gender she identifies with. In many Indian societies, there are males, females, and 'two-spirited people,' who are both masculine and feminine. Little Bear loves to hunt and fish and ride horses like her father. She will never be a Massachusetts housewife."

I found my admiration for Maria growing. It had to be difficult to endure societal disapproval of your marriage. It had to be even more difficult to endure societal disapproval of your daughter. Yet Maria held her head high. She made me think of the quote on a brass plaque that Mrs. Dean kept on her desk in our classroom:

> To be yourself in a world
> that is constantly trying
> to make you something else
> is the greatest accomplishment.
> — Ralph Waldo Emerson

"Do you consider yourself a Transcendentalist?" I asked Maria.

"Well, yes, but they're mostly too intellectual for me." Maria blushed. "I'm more of an activist. My heart goes out to the Indians and the Negroes, and women and children. I've had some success publishing stories and poems and tracts about the plight of the oppressed, but I don't have time for philosophizing. The Transcendentalists want philosophizing in their magazine."

"Magazine?" I echoed.

Maria nodded. "They call it *The Dial*." She dug through her magazine rack until she found the one she was looking for. "You know, as in a sundial? The concept for the magazine is explained on the inside cover."

She handed the magazine to me. I recognized it. It was the same magazine Mrs. Alcott had shared with me on our stagecoach ride to Concord—the one containing her husband's *Orphic Sayings*. It was folded open to the editor's introduction.

And so with diligent hands and good intent we present our *Dial*. We wish it may resemble that instrument that measures not hours but only rays of sunshine. Let it be one cheerful, rational voice amidst the din of mourners and polemics. Our chosen image is not the dead face of a clock or a stiff garden gnome. Our *Dial* is like the garden in which it sits. The suddenly awakened sleeper consults its moving shadow to learn what new life and growth is now arriving.

"Emerson wrote that introduction," Maria explained, "but he has handed over the role of editor to a friend of mine, Margaret Fuller. Do you know her?"

"Yes," I said. "We met her at a symposium at Emerson's house on Saturday evening."

"Oh!" Louisa May, who had drifted away from our conversation, was examining some framed sepia photographs on the wall on the other side of the dreamcatcher. She pointed at one of them. "Is this Little Bear?"

Maria nodded. "She's all grown up, isn't she?"

I rose to look. In the photograph was a young woman with a square jaw, a broad nose, and piercing eyes. Beneath the image was a ribbon-shaped illustration inscribed with the name "Evangeline Polis."

CHAPTER
TWENTY-SIX

Another *E*.

I barely tasted the huckleberry pie that Maria graciously served before we left. Though Maria was pleased with it, Louisa May and I were both too shaken by the discovery of the name *Evangeline* to enjoy it.

Without making our distress known to Maria, we decided that we could no longer put off our visit to Thoreau's cabin. We had a lot of new information that would help us determine whether or not he knew anything about the murder.

Maria indicated that we could get to Thoreau's cabin easily by following Sudbury Road out of town and making a left on the main road. Soon we would see the familiar path to Walden Pond.

After we left the Polis home, I elaborated a new possibility for the murder: "Little Bear and Thoreau share a deep love of nature and a hatred of greed. Thoreau falls in love with Little Bear because of her masculine traits but then comes to hate her because she's not actually a man."

"Maybe," Louisa May allowed. "But Little Bear doesn't strike me as the kind of woman who would wear an orange flowered skirt."

"Maybe she bought the skirt to make it into something else," I proposed. "Like a bag to hold the materials needed for the giant dreamcatcher. Maybe Thoreau had nothing to do with the murder. Maybe Little Bear was bringing her giant dreamcatcher to the woods, and the Wendigo got her."

Louisa May shot me a deadpan gaze. "You and I both know perfectly well that the Wendigo does not exist."

"How do you know?" I objected. "Things may be different here." I was careful not to make any direct reference to the dream, lest we get booted out.

Louisa May scowled uncomprehendingly. "What do you mean?"

"You know." I bugged my eyes out to indicate that I couldn't say more. *"Here."*

The creases in Louisa May's forehead multiplied.

"You know!" I repeated, growing frustrated. "Here in nineteenth-century Concord as opposed to *there* in the future world you talked about earlier, where you can buy any kind of berries you want all year long at the store."

Louisa May stopped walking and grabbed my shoulder. "Llew, that future world is just a dream."

I stared at her incredulously. She looked as though she believed what she was saying—that the life of TJ and Ivy was a dream, and our current life as Louisa May and Llew was real. Was she just acting her part to ensure that we wouldn't get booted out of the dream? Or had she somehow forgotten the truth?

I wanted to ask her, but I couldn't think how to do it without getting us booted out of the dream. I didn't want to go back to real life in the future. I wanted to stay here—forever.

"Okay, fine," I revised. "I guess I just want to say that things might be different in the woods."

"Well," Louisa May stubbornly declared, "I won't believe in any people-eating forest monster until I see one with my own eyes."

As I listened to Louisa May speaking, I realized that something about her had changed since that morning. She seemed so much more like Louisa May Alcott and so much less like Ivy dressed up as Louisa May Alcott. The dream was becoming more real.

Ivy had started dreaming the dream before me. What if, over time, it sucks you in, absorbs you, so that you get to a point at which you can no longer remember who you really are and therefore can no longer get yourself booted out?

That question unleashed a series of even more provocative questions: What if Louisa May was actually correct? What if the life of TJ was nothing but a dream about the future? What if I had really been Llew Willis all along? I felt my heart soar. Then we really could stay here forever!

It was a bright and breezy afternoon. Careless clouds drifted across a deep blue sky. The meadow alongside the road was humming with life. There were no cars with harried travelers zooming past us, just an occasional farm wagon clomping by. There were no billboards advertising junk food and porn shops, just untrimmed trees and bushes swaying in cosmic harmony.

"What are you grinning about?" Louisa May demanded. "I swear, Llew Willis, you are acting very strange today."

"Oh, I don't know," I replied, taking her hand. "Louisa May, I feel so lucky that I met your mother on that stagecoach and came to stay here in Concord with you instead of going on to Still River like I was supposed to. Just think how close I came to never meeting you!"

Louisa May smiled. "I bet you would have met a lot of prettier girls in Still River."

"Impossible!" I proclaimed. I stopped and made a move to put my arms around her—wanting very much to resume the moment that had been so rudely interrupted the day before—but she slipped away and started running. Holding her dress in one hand over her pantaloons, she was fast. I took off after her. She looked back, squealing with laughter, and then ran even faster. We had almost reached the trail to Thoreau's cabin. It was a beaten path through the meadow leading into the woods.

By the time we reached it, we were both breathing hard. Louisa May was slowing down. She was faster than me for sprinting, but I had greater endurance.

When I finally got close enough to grab her arm, she screamed and turned to fight me. I might have been worried if she hadn't been grinning from ear to ear.

"It will be my great pleasure to trounce you good, Mr. Willis." She threw herself at me, and soon we were both sprawled on the ground. She pounced on me like a kitten. Her goal seemed to be to pin me down until I said *uncle*, but I was so enjoying being pinned down that I didn't resist much.

"Well, then, Mr. Willis, since I know how much you love mud, let's just see how you like it up your nose!" Louisa May clawed a clump of grass out of the ground and dove toward my face.

"Okay, okay!" I protested, spattering mud on both of us as I barely deflected her assault. "Uncle! I am defeated."

Still straddling me, she discarded her weapon and shot both arms up in ecstatic victory. I propped myself up on one arm and reached my other hand out to wipe a speck of mud from her soft cheek. "I think you deserve a congratulatory kiss."

"Hmm."

"Or, maybe *I* deserve a *consolation* kiss."

"Hmm."

Louisa May thought about it a moment longer, squinting adorably in the shifting sunlight, and then she leaned in to kiss me on the lips. It was the sweetest moment of my entire life.

We stayed there on the grass, at the edge of the woods, under the expansive branches of an ancient oak tree, for a long time—until she knew she was mine, and I knew I was hers, and that was the way it was going to be.

CHAPTER
TWENTY-SEVEN

When we arrived at Thoreau's cabin, we could see immediately that something was wrong. The door was hanging open, swinging on its hinges. Papers were scattered on the step. A torn burlap sack was caught in a bush, dangling lifelessly, like the trampled flag of a besieged fortress.

"Mr. Thoreau?" I called.

No answer.

We called again, several times. We trotted down the hill to the shore of the lake and called across the water. No answer.

We didn't especially want to go into the cabin. What would we find in there? But we had to know if Thoreau was inside. He might need help.

I grabbed a heavy stick from the woodpile—the only available weapon. We snuck close to one of the windows and peered inside.

More disarray. The trapdoor to the cellar was open. A chair was knocked over. The bedding was half on the floor.

"Let's go inside," Louisa May whispered.

So we did. There were muddy footprints all over the floor. I knelt to examine them. Human shoes and dog paws—very large dog paws.

"Well, if you leave your door open, any stray animal might wander in," Louisa May pointed out.

I checked the door. It had no lock.

"Thoreau is living out here in the woods alone without a lock on his door?!" I exclaimed.

Louisa May shrugged. "You don't lock your tent when you go camping."

She had a point.

A feeling of madness filled the cabin. It was as though something unnatural, unholy, had passed through.

"When was the last full moon?" I asked.

"Not sure," Louisa May replied. "Why?"

"Because these pawprints are bigger than four inches across." I measured the clearest print I could find between my thumb and index finger and held my hand up for her to see the measurement. "I think it was a wolf."

She frowned. "I haven't heard reports of any wolves around Concord. There are a lot fewer of them than there used to be in these parts. Thoreau says all the logging is causing them to die out."

"What if it wasn't just a wolf? What if it was a werewolf?" I proposed. "Werewolves often keep their condition a secret, moving away from society without arousing suspicion until they can no longer control their moonlit rampages."

Louisa May snorted. "Oh, stop! Let's stick to the facts, please. Thoreau's rowboat is gone. Maybe he's out fishing, and some hobo broke in to steal food."

Just then a loud skittering noise made us jump.

I peered under the bed. Two bright little eyes peered back at me. "Sheesh!"

Louisa May bent to look. "It's Thoreau's mouse, Krishna. He must be terrified."

"Hey, Krishna," I called, moving the cot away from the wall to get a better look. "Can you tell us what happened here?"

Krishna came charging out from under the cot and scurried through the open trapdoor and down the tree trunk into the cellar.

"I suppose he's right," Louisa May remarked. "We need to go down there."

I knelt by the trapdoor. Although daylight had not completely faded, it was dark as midnight in the cellar. I wasn't going down there without a light.

I looked around. "Thoreau has to have a lantern around here somewhere," I muttered.

Louisa May and I swept our eyes around the room. There wasn't any place for a lantern to hide.

And then it came to me, hitting me like frying pan to the head. I looked straight up. Louisa May followed my gaze.

"Holy buttermilk," she breathed. "Thoreau has a garret."

Of course Thoreau has a garret!

Somewhere in my subconscious brain, I had known it all along. I had read it in his book *Walden; or, Life in the Woods* on the page that was bookmarked by the dreamcatcher:

> I have thus a tight shingled and plastered house, ten feet wide by fifteen long, and eight-feet posts, with a garret and a closet, a large window on each side, two trap doors, one door at the end, and a brick fireplace opposite.

Two trapdoors. Not one, but two. One for the cellar and one for the garret—a.k.a. the attic.

What did Thoreau keep in his attic? Probably a lantern. But the more important question was already thundering through my head: *What's in the garret of the twin cabin back in Red River, Louisiana? Is that where Ivy's missing painting is hidden? Of course! Safe and dry.*

Dumbstruck, I gazed at Louisa May.

"What?" she demanded.

I wanted to tell her. I could get us booted out of the dream right now and find the painting, solving that mystery once and for all. Ivy would be so pleased.

But I couldn't. I didn't want to. I refused to go back— not even to solve the mystery, not even to please Ivy. Louisa

May knew nothing of the painting, and she was all I cared about now.

"Nothing," I muttered, grabbing a chair to stand on.

I stood on the chair, pushed open the trapdoor, and peered into Thoreau's garret. There were two things up there: a tent and a lantern. In a compartment at the bottom of the lantern was a block of steel and some flint.

"What, no matches?" Louisa May complained. "I swear, Thoreau is living in the dark ages. They've been selling matches at the Concord General Store since I was a little girl. I still remember the first shipment. They sold out in twenty-four hours."

"You remember that?" I asked. I myself had no memory of Llew's childhood. On the contrary, I still had memories of TJ's childhood. For example, I remembered seeing Ivy and her granddad, Mr. Smith, walking to the bus stop each weekday for afternoon kindergarten.

"You probably got matches sooner, growing up in Boston," Louisa May remarked. "But the farmers out here in Concord were suspicious of them for a long time, thinking they were the work of the devil. Usually my family can't afford them, so I'm pretty good at flint. Come on, we'd better do it outside."

So we went outside. Since I didn't know anything about lighting a fire using flint and steel, I sat back and watched. I liked watching Louisa May—her graceful hands, her long neck, her glossy hair, pulled back in a French braid today, with many rebellious strands. To me, she was a living sculpture—a work of art. Though I felt my cheeks burn at these thoughts, I couldn't help thinking them.

Luckily, Louisa May was not paying attention to me. First she built a small pile of dry twigs and grass. Then she struck the flint—a black material—against the steel bar. Each time, a spark flew out. On the fourth strike, a spark landed in the tinder and lit a fire. After fanning the flames higher, she held a small stick in them until the end lit. Finally, she used the lit end of the stick to light the wick in the lamp.

"There!" Louisa May stood and stamped out her fire. "Now let's go see what's down in that cellar!"

CHAPTER
TWENTY-EIGHT

I went first, shimmying down the tree trunk into the cellar. After handing the lantern down to me, Louisa May followed. I held the lantern up high, and we looked around. It was just like the cellar in the twin cabin back in real life— if that really was real life.

Against the first wall was a crude, wooden shelf holding several jars, canisters, and burlap sacks. Two jars lay broken on the ground. The canisters on the lower shelves were tipped and dumped, their contents—dried corn, rice, and flour—scattered.

Against the second wall was a loose pile of rough wool blankets. Louisa May bent and pawed through them. She encountered nothing other than blanket—until her hand caught on something soft and silky. It was an orange headscarf. She held it up, and I brought the lantern close.

"Whoa," I breathed. "That's an awful nice match for the orange flowered skirt."

"It's not an exact match," Louisa May hedged, fingering the square pattern on the scarf, "but to someone who really likes orange, it might have made a good complement for the skirt." She stuffed it into her pocket for future reference.

Against the third wall was a battered wooden trunk, not locked. I set the lantern on the ground and hefted it open. Inside was a pile of men's clothing: trousers, boots, shirts, a wool coat, a hat, socks, and "drawers"—ankle-length underwear with three buttons closing a center fly. These could have been Thoreau's own winter garments. Unlike the trunk in the twin cabin, this trunk held no soldier uniforms. Of course not—the Civil War hadn't happened yet.

Against the fourth wall was a little door. Ah, the tunnel. The door stood wide open. Had someone busted in? Or had someone fled out? I knelt on the ground to look for footprints, but no tracks were discernible in the hard-packed dirt.

We still had no clues to Thoreau's whereabouts. All that was left was the tunnel. What was the tunnel really for? And where did it lead? Thoreau could be in there.

We had a lantern. We had to brave it.

It wasn't easy. We had to crawl. The floor, the walls, and the ceiling were all made of the same hard-packed dirt. I went first. I had to move slowly in order to keep the lantern from snuffing out. Also, we were supposed to be looking for clues along the way. To be honest, after the first few feet, all I could think about was escaping alive.

About halfway through, as the tunnel began to bend, I heard Louisa May starting to breath hard behind me. She stopped advancing. I didn't want to stop. I wanted to keep going—as fast as I could. But I couldn't go without her. I stopped.

"Llew," she whimpered, "I can't do it. I...." More hard breathing. "I...."

She was going to hyperventilate. The space was too small for me to turn around. I felt it closing in on me. I took a deep breath.

"Llew?" she wailed.

"I'm here." I backed up and reached my hand back to touch her shoulder in the flickering light. "I'm right here, Louisa May. It's okay."

The flickering light was making me feel dizzy. I closed my eyes. How long before the fumes from the lantern would make us pass out?

"Louisa May." I squeezed her shoulder. "I want you to close your eyes. Can you do that? Close your eyes tight."

"I can't!" she rasped. "I'm scared!"

"I know," I whispered. "It helps to close your eyes. Can you do it, please?"

After making a strange mewing sound, she responded, "Okay."

"Now keep your eyes closed tight, and follow my voice. I'm going to take us out of here. You must keep your eyes closed. I want you to imagine the stars over our heads. The stars really are over our heads, you know. You just can't see them right now, but you can imagine them. So tell me what you see."

"I can't," she protested.

"Yes, you can," I commanded. "Tell me about the stars."

"Um," she croaked. "I...I see the Big Dipper."

"Yes." As soon as she started talking, I started crawling again. "And what else? Follow me, and tell me more."

"Um." She started crawling. "I see the Little Dipper."

"Yes." As soon as I rounded the bend, I could see dim light at the end of the tunnel. It was almost sunset, but the hole was on the north side of the hill, catching the day's final rays of light.

"I see the North Star," Louisa May continued, her voice growing stronger.

As we neared the end of the tunnel, it grew narrower. I was on my elbows now, clawing my way forward commando-style. I squinted at the hole ahead. I couldn't tell how big it was. What if it was too small for me to fit through?

I stopped, breathing hard. Sweat dripped down my forehead, stinging my eyes. A terrifying vision flashed across my mind: Louisa May and I, trapped in the tunnel, the walls collapsing around us, suffocating us, burying us alive.

Casting a glance back at Louisa May, I hit the lantern against a stone protruding from the wall and knocked its flickering light out. I froze, blinking in the dark, waiting for Louisa May to panic. But she didn't notice, evidently because she still had her eyes shut tight.

As my eyes grew accustomed to the darkness, I could see the end of the tunnel more clearly. I could see out of the hole. I could see a star.

Louisa May, still crawling, bumped into my feet. "What's wrong, Llew? Are you okay? Can you see the North Star?"

"Yes, I think I actually can." I started crawling again. This time I didn't stop until my hands touched grass on the edge of the hole and I began pulling myself out. I felt like a baby being born out of the Earth herself. With one last heave, I tumbled out of the tunnel and came to rest on my back on a steep, rocky hill. A moment later, Louisa May tumbled out after me. I heard her gulping in the fresh air, crying out with relief.

When my own heart finally stopped pounding, I sat up to look around. There weren't many trees on this side of the hill. The horizon stretched out in every direction. Walden Pond lay below us. Beyond it, thick forest. The setting sun threw streaks of purple and gold across the sky to the west. To the east, the sky grew black as stars blinked to life. I'd never seen the stars shine so bright as they did here in the nineteenth century, before the invention of city lights.

Louisa May sat up. I scooched over to put my arm around her. We didn't say anything. We didn't need to. We had never felt so glad to be alive.

Drinking in the magical lightshow unfolding before us, I didn't just feel alive; I felt more alive than I ever had before. My personal self seemed to bleed into the hillside. I was no longer an individual lifeform at all but a part of the life of nature as a whole. I disappeared into a sea of being, vibrating with eternal energy. Shedding all identity of my own, I saw everything. I became a transparent eyeball.

CHAPTER
TWENTY-NINE

A bright moon rose that night, enabling Louisa May and me to walk home fearlessly, almost in a trance. Perhaps because of my new alliance with nature, I noted that the moon was not quite full. Had it been full on Friday night, the night of the murder?

According to the legends I knew from comic books and movies, werewolves come about due to an affliction called lycanthropy. People with this affliction grow fur and fangs under the light of the moon and then become irrationally violent. The fuller the moon, the worse it gets.

If I believed that I was coming down with lycanthropy, I might build myself a cabin in the woods. From there, I could terrorize rabbits and deer rather than my family and friends. I didn't share this insight with Louisa May, since it was impossible for me to convey to her why supernatural explanations were fair game in this case.

When we arrived home, Mrs. Alcott scolded us for missing dinner but grudgingly served us some snacks before sending us off to bed. Being early risers, the other members of the household were already asleep. Mrs. Alcott was gratified to learn that we had helped Maria bake charity pies.

She said we could deal with Thoreau's disappearance in the morning.

After a long, deep sleep, Louisa May and I spoke to her father over breakfast. Though Bronson Alcott was still shaken from his encounter with the dead body in the woods, he proposed that the three of us go together to tell Emerson about Thoreau's disappearance. The cabin had clearly been broken into, and it was on Emerson's property. Although Sheriff Staples could not be fully trusted, Emerson needed to be informed.

We could see a two-horse wagon parked outside the Emerson home as we drew near. A number of men were milling about on the lawn amid piles of baggage and crates full of supplies.

"Oh, right," Mr. Alcott muttered in annoyance. "The philosophers' camping trip."

I didn't recognize any of the men until I caught sight of the painters William James Stillman and his young protégé Ring. Stillman was the main organizer, pointing and shouting and loading bags onto the wagon. Ring lolled on the porch steps, studying the group, smoking a long pipe. He blew some smoke rings. They floated lazily away.

Perhaps the stuff in Ring's pipe was not tobacco. His haunted eyes suggested that he somehow knew that this reality was not quite reality.

Is it possible that other real people are playing characters in this dream? I wondered to myself.

It *was* possible, if Ivy had shown the dreamcatcher to someone else. Anyone who touched it could be in the dream with us. But I doubted that Ivy had shown anyone else the dreamcatcher, given that her mother had strictly forbidden her from removing anything from the cabin.

Ring was probably just a character in the dream.

It occurred to me with a pang that the people around me weren't really people at all. If this was a dream, then they were all just imaginary—based on historical people, yes, but still just projections of the imagination—my imagination and Ivy's imagination. The dreamcatcher somehow allowed me and Ivy to unite our imaginations in a realistic way. In fact, the dream was becoming so realistic for Ivy that she wasn't even Ivy anymore.

Does that mean Ivy has become imaginary? Is Louisa May only imaginary? Why haven't I been absorbed into the dream yet? What will it be like to be imaginary? Or could I turn this dream into reality and turn my old reality into a dream through sheer force of will?

So many questions about the metaphysics of the situation wafted through my mind. I didn't have time to answer them. I was following Mr. Alcott through the front door, and we ran into Emerson coming down the staircase.

A surprised smile stole over Emerson's face when he caught sight of us. "Changed your mind about the camping trip, Bronson?"

"No, sir," Mr. Alcott replied. "I've come to change yours." He proceeded, with our help, to explain Thoreau's disappearance.

"Bronson," Emerson sighed, "Thoreau often takes his boat up the Assabet River for days at a time. There's a mill up there that he likes to visit—American Gunpowder. He sits on the cliff and watches their research team blow things up. This time of year he sleeps on a blanket under the light of the moon without even a tent."

"Did he by chance write you a note?" I asked. I was thinking of the unfinished frenemy poem.

"No." Emerson shrugged. "It sounds like an animal got into his cabin while he was away. A hobo could have stolen the food in the cellar. I'm sure he's fine."

"Normally, I would agree," Bronson conceded. "But with that murder—"

"Completely unrelated," Emerson snapped, impatient to resume packing for the trip.

Louisa May pulled the silk headscarf out of her pocket. "We found this in Thoreau's cellar."

Emerson's eyes flickered. The headscarf's screaming orange color could not help but bring back images of the shredded skirt the four of us had seen strewn about the woods.

"Emerson!" It was William James Stillman calling from the front yard.

Emerson set his jaw, a gesture that conveyed his final answer loud and clear. "If you will please excuse me," he said, brushing past us, "I still have a lot of packing to do."

We followed Emerson back out the front door.

Margaret Fuller had arrived. She was wearing a broad-brimmed hat, a knee-length skirt over leggings, and a pair of heavy-duty men's boots. She brandished a walking stick in one hand; with the other, she held a canvas bag over her shoulder. Standing as proud as a Girl Scout in the middle of the front yard, she grinned her toothy grin at Emerson.

William James Stillman hooked his thumb at her sheepishly. "She says she's coming."

Emerson threw back his head and laughed.

Margaret's grin faded. "What's so funny? You know I wouldn't miss this for the world."

Emerson folded his arms across his chest. "Absolutely not."

The campers began gathering around.

"And why not?" Margaret demanded.

"Because," Emerson hedged, "you're a woman. That's why."

"Hypocrite!" Margaret cried. "You say the soul needs to immerse itself in nature. Well, women have souls, too!"

As I watched Margaret unravel, it occurred to me that the Girl Scouts hadn't yet been invented.

"We don't want a scandal, Margaret," Emerson chided. "You know what people will say."

"To the devil with people!" Margaret threw her stick and her bag down with surprising violence. "I'm so sick and tired of hearing you urging fearless originality and then cowering like a little boy behind old societal biases."

Margaret's words hit Emerson like a slap in the face. You could almost hear the crowd "oooooh" at the assault.

Emerson just stared at her, torn between fighting back and retreating.

"I am a journalist!" Margaret marched up to Emerson and tried to get in his face, but she was too short, and so she shook her fist at him instead. "Horace Greely has hired me to go to Italy this fall to cover the revolution. I'll be the first female war correspondent in history. And you won't let me cover your stupid camping trip?"

Emerson shook his head. "We don't want to be 'covered.'"

"You're famous philosophers," she countered. "You're going camping. That's news. People want to know!"

"*Now* look who's catering to society," Emerson observed, his eyebrows arched.

"I'll show society that women can camp, all right," Margaret bellowed. "Women can do anything they set their minds to. Let them be sea captains if they like!"

"Fine," Emerson barked. "You do that. You go camping, Margaret. Just not with us."

"Fine!" Margaret roared. "I will!" She snatched her things off the ground and charged away.

Louis Agassiz, the famous biologist we had met at the Saturday symposium, had arrived in a carriage of his own while we were in the house. He held his hands above his head and applauded Emerson with bravado. This released the other campers from their shocked silence. They began to murmur and chuckle. William James Stillman came over and clapped Emerson on the back. Emerson's response was not as jocular as Stillman would have liked.

Bronson Alcott scowled at Stillman and took off after Margaret.

CHAPTER
THIRTY

Louisa May and I took off after Mr. Alcott and Margaret. Margaret stomped along. Mr. Alcott shuffled beside her, head bent, speaking low, as though calming a spooked horse.

"And how were your Conversations this week?" he was asking her as we caught up.

"Excellent," Margaret sniffed. "Elizabeth Cady Stanton and Lucretia Mott were there. They're getting ready to organize the world's first Women's Rights Convention in Seneca Falls. After my Conversations, I attended a dinner at the Parker House, where I conversed for some time with Edgar Allen Poe and Walt Whitman."

"Extraordinary!" Mr. Alcott exclaimed.

Margaret shrugged imperiously. "I now know all the people worth knowing in America, and I find no intellect comparable to my own."

Mr. Alcott chuffed. "I'm so grateful for your self-confidence, Margaret. Without it, you would never have had the courage to publish *Woman in the Nineteenth Century*. That book is truly the beginning of women's liberation in this country."

"The Negro, the Indian, and women are all in the same oppressed boat," Margaret pronounced. "We all have souls, the same as the white man. That makes us equal. It's time we were treated so."

"Hip, hip, hooray!" Louisa May trumpeted.

Margaret smiled, her spirit lifting.

When we arrived at the Alcott home, Mrs. Alcott invited Margaret to stay for lemonade. We sat in a crazy gazebo that Mr. Alcott had built out of driftwood in the back yard. Louisa May begged Margaret to share a favorite part of her book with us. Margaret was happy to oblige and paraphrased from memory.

Who is woman in the nineteenth century?

The lover, the poet, and the artist are likely to view her nobly. The father and the philosopher have some chance of viewing her with generosity. The man of the world, however, views her only with an eye to his own interest.

Under these circumstances, we welcome the changes demanded by the champions of woman. These changes are signs of the times. Every arbitrary barrier must be thrown down. Every path must be laid open— as freely to woman as to man.

When these changes are accomplished, there will be a temporary uproar. Once it subsides, however, beauty will crystallize in more pure and diverse forms.

When these changes are accomplished, divine energy will pervade nature to a degree unknown in the history of former ages. Male and female spheres will no longer collide discordantly. A ravishing harmony will ensue.

When will the world be ripe for these changes? Only when inward and outward freedom shall be acknowledged as a right, not yielded as a concession, for woman as much as for man.

The friend of the Negro understands that one man cannot, by right, hold another in bondage. Likewise, the friend of woman understands that man cannot, by right, lay even well-meant restrictions on her. If the Negro be a soul dressed in flesh, if woman be a soul dressed in flesh, then they are accountable to one divine master only. There is but one law for all souls.

Male and female are often represented as two sides of a great divide. But, in fact, they are constantly passing into one another. Fluid hardens to solid; solid rushes to fluid. There is no wholly masculine man, no purely feminine woman.

Let us be wise: let us not impede the soul. Let the soul do its work. Let us have one creative energy, one unending revelation. Let this revelation take what form it will. Let us not bind it by the past to man or woman, black or white!

Margaret ended her paraphrase with a shake of her fist.

We all applauded.

Louisa May was on the edge of her chair, ready to jump up and shout. It was as though Margaret's nascent feminism was the most exciting thing she had ever heard.

I had to remind myself what was going on in the nineteenth century to understand why. In the nineteenth century, women were not allowed into the universities for higher education, they were not allowed to seek political office or vote, and they were not allowed to own property. A woman's whole role in life was to assist her husband so that *he* could accomplish important things in the world. Women were limited to the endless cleaning, cooking, and childrearing work of the domestic sphere.

Margaret was a true exception. Without women like her, nothing would have changed.

It occurred to me that she was clearly right to argue that the emancipation of women was better for both sexes. I thought of my dream character, Llew Willis. According to the papers in my satchel, he was destined for Harvard University, just like Emerson and Thoreau had been. It would be a bummer to go off to Harvard, learn all kinds of interesting things, and then come back to marry someone who was deliberately kept clueless. It would be a bummer to marry someone who was more like a servant than a partner.

I looked at Louisa May. As if reading my thoughts, her eyes misted up, and she looked away.

"You know, Margaret," Mrs. Alcott said, "I'm so glad that you brought up the connection between the 'woman question' and the 'slavery question' because so many people, even good-hearted reformers, try to say that they are separate issues. But really they are united by a common bottom line: human rights."

"Well said," Mr. Alcott concurred. "I've been thinking about the idea of human rights a lot lately. I've been reading everything I can get my hands on. It's such a noble idea—the noblest. But it's quite difficult to prove that human rights actually exist or should exist. I mean, as far as scientific knowledge goes, all animal life is a matter of survival—everyone takes whatever they can get. By this logic, if the Americans of the South can enslave the Africans, then why shouldn't they? Why shouldn't the more powerful rule the less powerful?"

"The idea of human rights will never be proven scientifically," Margaret asserted. "Belief in them is a faith that comes from religion."

Mr. Alcott nodded. "I noticed you mention that human beings are accountable to 'one divine master' in your paraphrase just now. Elsewhere in your book you talk about 'the son of God.' Here's where I take issue with you, Margaret. I think that as long as you keep conceiving of God as 'the father' and 'the master' and 'the son,' you're never going to shake the old masculine hierarchy."

"Don't forget that I grew up Unitarian, Bronson," Margaret admonished. "Jesus was a human prophet, in my view, not God himself."

"Well, that's a start," Mr. Alcott conceded. "Long ago, Christians proposed that God is a Trinity—God the Father, God the Son, and God the Holy Spirit. More recently, the Unitarians rejected God the Son, but they still cling to God the Father. As Transcendentalists, I think we need to go the other route: reject God the Father along with God the

Son and stick with just God the Holy Spirit instead. God is the divine soul in us all. It's what makes us equal. It's what gives us rights. If you ask for something from God the Father, it's just a concession. What's to prevent God from giving rights to the *fathers* of the world and not to *you*?"

"Oh, Bronson," Margaret protested, "everyone knows that the word *father* is just a metaphor for God."

Louisa May, following the conversation closely, plucked up her nerve to chime in. "Suppose you said 'God the Parent' in order to avoid the masculine conception of God. That would still imply that you think God is outside of you—a separate being that created you. But maybe God isn't distinct from us at all. In his essay "Nature," Emerson says that our souls are divine—that we are all particles of God."

Mrs. Alcott grinned. "Are you a particle of God or not, Margaret?"

Margaret snorted. "I'm not going to be a particle of anything that Emerson is a particle of!"

Mr. Alcott laughed. "Margaret, do you know who I have found to be the best author on human rights?"

"Who?"

"The famous and recently deceased Unitarian minister William Ellery Channing."

"Oh, you mean in his book *Slavery*?"

Mr. Alcott nodded. "I gave the copy I was reading back to Emerson, but let me read you my notes from his chapter on rights.

C H A P T E R
T H I R T Y - O N E

SLAVERY

Chapter Two: Rights
by William Ellery Channing

The first question for a rational being is not "What is profitable?" but rather "What is right?" Duty must be first among the objects of human thought. This is the most fundamental law of reason. If we inquire first for our interests and then for our duties, we will make fatal mistakes.

As soon as we become conscious of duty, a kindred consciousness springs up—the feeling that we are responsible for what we do. This feeling gives rise to dignity, which is the intuitive conviction that we are essentially equal to everyone else.

If we are all equally responsible, then we all have equal duties. The same voice forbidding me to injure others forbids others to injure me. This voice is conscience. In revealing the moral law, conscience does not speak for myself only but speaks as a Universal Legislator of human rights.

There is no deeper principle in human nature than conscience. So profound is its awareness of human rights that centuries of oppression have nowhere wholly stifled it. But since centuries of oppression have somewhat stifled our conscience, we must ask: What exactly are our rights as human beings?

It is difficult to define human rights because spiritual matters cannot be weighed and measured like material things. Although volumes could be written about human rights, perhaps they may all be summarized in one sentence: *Human beings have the right to promote happiness and virtue for themselves and others.*

Happiness are virtue are the great purpose of our existence. Our powers are designed to make ourselves and others better in every way, insofar as we are able.

Just as each of us is bound to work for our own and others' good, each of us is bound to leave all others free for the accomplishment of this end. Everyone who uses his or her powers without obstructing others has a sacred right to be equally unobstructed.

That is the grand, all-encompassing right of human nature. We should all revere it. Asserting it for ourselves and for all, we should bear solemn testimony against every infraction of it.

From the grand right of human nature, particular rights may easily be deduced. For example:

- Everyone has the right to develop his or her intellect.

- Everyone has the right to be respected as a member of the community.

- Everyone has the right to be protected by impartial laws.

- Everyone has the right to be exempted from coercion and punishment, as long as he or she respects the rights of others.

- Everyone has the right to an equivalent for his or her labor.

- Everyone has the right to enjoy family relations.

These are just a few of our human rights—and if so, what a grievous wrong is slavery!

Mr. Alcott cleared his throat and took a sip of lemonade.

Mrs. Alcott took advantage of the opportunity to cut in. "Imagine replacing that last line with: 'These are just a few of our human rights—and if so, how grievously wronged is woman!'"

Mr. Alcott nodded. "I could go on, but I think that's enough to give you the gist of Channing's argument. I summarize it like this." He looked back at his notes.

1. Human nature produces conscience.

2. Conscience produces duty.

3. Duty produces responsibility.

4. Responsibility produces equality.

5. Equality produces human rights.

6. Therefore, by transitivity, human nature produces human rights.

Mr. Alcott looked up. "The only problem is that Channing, being a Unitarian, adds a step prior to step 1: *God creates human nature.* This opens the door to the possibility, exploited throughout history, that God wants a hierarchy among humans on Earth. He created male nature, female nature, African nature, etc., with different duties and responsibilities, making them equal only *within their class*, not across the board.

"Replace this Unitarian starting point with a Transcendentalist starting point: *A single divine or holy spirit constitutes all human nature.* With this starting point, there's no basis for introducing a hierarchy of classes. Our souls are all literally the same."

Though I found Mr. Alcott's analysis compelling, it still left me with a burning question, which I plucked up the courage to ask: "If you don't have God creating nature, then what does? If there's no God outside of us, then how did the universe itself get started?"

"It didn't," Mr. Alcott answered. "The universe has always existed."

I stared at him, waiting for him to defend his statement.

"If you can conceive of a God without a beginning," he prodded, "then you can conceive of a universe without a beginning. Or did your God have a beginning—in which case, who created *him*?"

I didn't know what to say to that. I knew from a recent conversation with Ivy that she was of the same opinion.

Mr. Alcott looked up, following a hawk gliding across the sky. "We Transcendentalists don't need a creator god at all."

On that note, Mrs. Alcott picked up a copy of *The Dial* from the table and began to read:

INCARNATION.

The world has been forever pulsing, like an eternal heart. Spirit courses through its mystic veins. We ride the powerful waves, whose flux is life, reflux death, efflux thought, and conflux light. Our bodies are the atoms of God.

"Oh, please!"Margaret erupted. "Enough with Bronson's *Orphic Sayings*. They're the laughing stock of the magazine."

"All they needed was a decent editor," Mr. Alcott shot back.

This sour exchange might have turned into an ugly fight if I hadn't noticed something just then. I was thinking about the name *William Ellery Channing*, the author of the book on slavery that Mr. Alcott had just shared with us. I pinned my eyes on Louisa May. "Didn't Thoreau give us a poem by this same Channing fellow? Remember? The one about death and the afterlife?"

Louisa May squinted uncertainly. "That poem is by Larry Channing. I believe he's the nephew of William Ellery Channing. I have my copy of the poem here." She pulled the paper out of her pocket for the others to read.

A Poet's Hope
by Larry Channing

Lady—
There's one old hope all mortals have:
Some mercy and a resting place,
A daisy-strewn and grassy grave.
But does this hope improve our race?
No, Ma'am—
I seek no resting place for good;
I'm onward to the farthest shores.
So lift me up, unceasing flood,
Which from the purest fountain pours.
I smile, for new hope grows in me:
If my boat sinks, tis to another sea.

"My sister's husband wrote that poem," Margaret informed us. "It may allude to death and the afterlife, but it's really about marriage and separation. My sister found a copy of it on her husband's pillow Sunday morning—with him gone. He's been especially distant and uncommunicative lately. I think he's left her for good."

I read the poem again. So Channing hadn't made a grammatical mistake after all. The word *Lady* wasn't meant to personify poetry; it was meant to address his wife.

"What will poor Lennie do?" Mrs. Alcott exclaimed. "Abandoned with two baby girls!"

Margaret shrugged. "I sent the three of them to Cambridgeport this morning to stay with relatives for a while."

"The Poet of Concord," Mr. Alcott clucked, "off on a whim again."

"Oh, he's infuriating all right," Margaret grumbled as she took a closer look at Louisa May's copy of the poem. She pointed to the line under the title where Louisa May had written "by Larry Channing."

Louisa May frowned at the page, not understanding why Margaret was pointing.

"His name isn't Larry," Margaret informed us. "You must have misheard Thoreau because of his accent, which probably made *Ellery* sound like *'Llery*. Ellery was given the same name as his famous uncle, William Ellery Channing, but he has always gone by his middle name in order to avoid confusion."

"*Ellery*?" Louisa May gasped.

She and I were thinking the same thing: another *E*.

CHAPTER
THIRTY-TWO

"You two look like you've just seen a ghost," Mrs. Alcott declared.

"You certainly do," Margaret concurred, her eyes darting between us. "What's going on?"

Louisa May and I locked eyes. We knew it was time to get some help with our investigation.

Louisa May turned over the paper on which she'd copied Channing's poem, revealing the unfinished frenemy poem by Thoreau:

> Surely, surely, thou wilt trust me
> When I say thou dost disgust me.
> O, I hate thee with a hate
> That would fain annihilate;
> Yet sometimes against my will,
> My dear E, I love thee still.
> If thou won't s

"I accidentally took this from Mr. Thoreau the same day he was arrested," Louisa May confessed. "Llew and I were wondering whether Mr. Thoreau was somehow involved in the death of that unidentified woman in the woods, especially now that he's missing and his cabin's been broken into.

We've been trying to figure out who 'E' refers to. Maybe it was Ellery."

I turned the page back over and looked at Channing's poem again. "What if this poem really *is* about death rather than marriage? That last line: 'If my boat sinks, 'tis to another sea.' What if Channing is worried that he's in danger?"

Margaret's fur was bristling. "I'm going to find him." She stood.

"We'll go with you," Louisa May declared, jumping up. "But where is he?"

"According to rumors," Margaret replied, "he went to Fruitlands."

"Fruitlands?!" all three Alcotts echoed in shocked unison.

"What's Fruitlands?" I demanded.

As it turned out, Fruitlands was the name of the farm in Still River where the Alcotts once lived. But Fruitlands was no ordinary farm. It was the site of their experiment in communal living.

The story of Fruitlands is so bizarre that it seems like the stuff of dreams, but it was real. Here's the short version of the story, which I later researched:

> During the 1830s, Bronson Alcott's Transcendentalist ideas caught on with some reformers in England, who established an experimental community and school in a large house. In honor of Bronson Alcott, they named it Alcott House.

The members of Alcott House practiced strict vegetarianism, rejected the Victorian dress code, and adopted progressive educational methods. When Bronson Alcott came to visit Alcott House, he and one of its members, Charles Lane, decided to start an even more radical community back in the United States.

Since Alcott was penniless and didn't believe in ownership anyway, Lane purchased the farm: ninety acres for $1,800. They named it "Fruitlands" with the idea that they would eat only fruit and a few grains that they were able to grow themselves. No coffee, tea, alcohol, or animal products (including honey) would be allowed. They would not exploit any animal labor to work the farm. They would rise early, bathe in cold water, and spend the day purifying themselves through contemplation and honest labor. They would be economically independent of the corrupt society around them.

Fruitlands attracted fourteen residents, who lived together in the modest farmhouse. They called themselves the "consociate family" (*consociate* means to spend time with others in fellowship). Six of them were the Alcotts. Among the rest were Charles Lane and his son, one nudist, one crazy man, one ex-con, one coprolalic (someone who involuntarily uses foul language—often a symptom of mental illness or brain disease), one self-educated Kantian philosopher, and one woman who was soon kicked out of Fruitlands because she was caught eating a piece of fish.

The community lasted only half of a year, from July to December, when the consociates began quarreling and ran out of food. The only actual farmer among them was the ex-con—a crusty old veteran of the Revolutionary War named Joseph Palmer.

Palmer was a highly unusual and strangely admirable criminal. Ever since serving his country as a soldier, he had stubbornly insisted on wearing a long beard. At that time in New England, long beards were unfashionable to the point of being offensive. Bearded men were widely perceived as a threat to common decency. Palmer endured much criticism for his unruly facial hair.

One day a posse of angry townsmen jumped Palmer with scissors and a razor, attempting to pin him down and shave his face. Palmer fought back with his jackknife, injured some of his attackers, and was consequently arrested. For many months Palmer languished in jail, suffering abuse and inadequate food because he refused to shave his beard and pay the $10 fine the judge unjustly ordered him to pay.

https://en.wikipedia.org/wiki/Joseph_Palmer
(communard)#/media/File:Joseph_Palmer,_Fruitlands.jpg

Joseph Palmer's personal experience with injustice made him the most devoted resident of Fruitlands. After the community fell apart that winter, he scraped together enough money to buy the farm, turning it into a refuge for social reformers and outcasts of every kind.

But I didn't know all that at the time. All I knew was what I gathered from the ensuing discussion among the Alcotts and Margaret. According to them, at the beginning of the Fruitlands experiment, Emerson and Channing had visited the farm together, and they had applauded the courage and originality of the consociates. Palmer would undoubtedly welcome Channing back, even if Channing was fleeing his family responsibilities. Palmer would also remember Louisa May with fondness. She was only ten years old during the Fruitlands experiment—a helpful girl who endured hardship due to her father's extreme idealism. Palmer would surely welcome us for a visit, provided that we didn't persecute Channing.

Mr. and Mrs. Alcott were not ready to revisit the site of their failed experiment. The failure had been especially traumatic for Bronson, who had mourned the death of his dream by standing in a corner and starving himself for a week. But Mr. and Mrs. Alcott permitted Louisa May and me to accompany Margaret to Fruitlands, as long as we returned the following day.

CHAPTER
THIRTY-THREE

After throwing some supplies into overnight bags, the three of us caught the stagecoach and rode the three-hour leg of the journey to Still River that I would have ridden the previous week, had I not injured my hand and gotten off early in Concord.

We were alone in the stagecoach except for two old men. (Were they the same two old men who had traveled with Mrs. Alcott and me the week before?) They snoozed on the opposite bench, occasionally shouting into each other's deaf ears.

Margaret sat on our bench with her back against the window so she could face us. She was bursting with something important, which she would not say until we waved goodbye to Mr. Alcott at the station.

"There's something else you should know," she rasped. "Ellery Channing is not the only one heading for Still River. The philosophers' camping trip is on its way there, too."

How did Margaret know this? Because William James Stillman, being a famous painter, had attended the same Parker House dinner in Boston where Margaret had met

Edgar Allen Poe and Walt Whitman. She had heard Stillman boasting about the philosophers' camping trip over dessert.

"I don't think the Still River connection is a coincidence," Margaret asserted. "I think there's a big story here, and I need your help to find out what it is. It's going to be dangerous. Do you understand me?"

Louisa May and I nodded, galvanized, anxious to hear what she had already learned.

The philosophers' plan was to ride their sturdy, horse-drawn cart, full of supplies, to Wolf Swamp Gate in Still River, where they would camp for the night. The next morning, their Native American guides would arrive with canoes. Together they would paddle north, down the Nashua River to the Merrimack River, to the Pemigewasset River, to Fitchburg. In Fitchburg, after a night's rest, they would board the Fitchburg Railroad and ride all day to Lake George, where they would board a steamship to Keeseville, the Gateway to the great Adirondack Mountain Range—the pinnacle of unspoiled American wilderness. From Keeseville, their guides would lead them to a remote campsite at Follensbee Pond.

"Follensbee Pond is *way* up north, almost to the Canadian border," Margaret pointed out, "which would make it an appealing destination for a fugitive, if you think about it."

"Are the philosophers harboring a fugitive?!" I asked.

Margaret shrugged suggestively, clearly enjoying the building drama. "The party consists of twelve Transcendentalists. They are philosophers in the broad sense of the word." She pulled a folded piece of paper from her pocket and read the list of camping trip participants aloud:

- Two writers: Ralph Waldo Emerson and James Russell Lowell

- Two scientists: Louis Agassiz and Jeffries Wyman

- Three lawyers: Ebenezer Hoar, Horatio Woodman, and John Holmes

- Three doctors: Estes Howe, Amos Binney, and Amos's brother Fuller

- Two painters: William James Stillman and his young apprentice Ring

"I don't have the names of the Indian guides they're meeting up with," Margaret noted, "but Joe Polis is probably one of them."

"Yes," Louisa May confirmed. "Joe's going."

I did a double-take at Louisa May. "How do you know that?"

"Because he said so."

"When?" I demanded.

"Um, well," Louisa May stammered, "when he stopped home yesterday. I guess you and Maria were upstairs looking for the third rolling pin. Joe came in the back door to get his rifle. He was in a hurry, but he had some kind of tent slung over his shoulder. So I asked him if he was going on the philosophers' camping trip."

"Louisa May, this is important." I grabbed her shoulders and made her look me in the eye. "Did you say anything else to Joe?"

"I don't think so." She shrugged defensively. "I don't really remember."

"Try to remember!"

"Stop it, Llew. You're scaring me."

"I'm sorry. It's okay. I just...." My voice trailed off. I couldn't say any more out loud. I just wanted to know whether she'd said something anachronistic that had gotten Ivy booted out of the dream. It would be so easy to slip up! For example, what if she'd said, *"Did you go* on the philosophers' camping trip?" instead of *"Are you going* on the philosophers' camping trip?" Would that be anachronistic enough to offend the dreamcatcher?

You must have said something wrong! I was gazing at Louisa May, screaming those words in my head. I said nothing out loud. When she gazed back at me, she seemed as lifeless as a paper doll.

At that moment I knew exactly what had happened. While I was upstairs getting the rolling pin with Maria, Ivy had gotten booted out of the dream. That explained why Louisa May suddenly seemed so much more like a nineteenth-century girl and so much less like a twenty-first-century girl in period costume.

My heart sank. I really was alone in this reality. Everyone else was imaginary. Everything that had happened between me and Louisa May in the woods the day before had been fake. I would never be absorbed into the dream. For as long as I avoided anachronisms, I could keep dreaming of Louisa May, but I would never be like her. She would always be a projection of my imagination.

So be it, I resolved. *What's the difference? It's like boxed mashed potatoes: with a little practice at self-deception and a little extra butter, you can convince yourself they're just as good as the real thing.*

Louisa May's lovely face was puckered with bewildered concern. "What is it, Llew? What are you thinking about?"

"Never mind," I replied, smiling bravely. "I was just trying to sort out my metaphysics."

"Oh, okay." She patted my knee and turned to look out the window. But it seemed to me as though she slipped right out the window and tumbled away, like an embroidered handkerchief, into the distant past.

CHAPTER
THIRTY-FOUR

We arrived at Fruitlands that evening. It was a two-story, ramshackle farmhouse at the end of a deeply rutted dirt driveway. A man with a long gray beard sat rocking in a rocking chair on the side porch. He eyed us curiously as we approached, without getting up.

"Mr. Palmer?" Louisa May waved. "It's me, Louisa May Alcott. Do you remember me?"

Joseph Palmer stopped rocking and leaned forward, squinting at us from beneath bushy eyebrows. It took him a moment to recognize Louisa May from the girl she used to be.

"Why," he exclaimed, "little Loulou! How nice of you to come back and see us!"

Louisa May ran to him for a hug. She was not little compared to him anymore. The two were about the same height.

Palmer squeezed her tight. "Who are your friends?" he asked.

Louisa May introduced us. As we were talking, a black woman wearing a turquoise headscarf and hoop earrings came to the door. She stood like a lioness at the mouth of her den, looking us over.

"You okay, Joseph?" she purred.

"Yes, dear, thank you," Palmer replied. "It's an old friend, along with her beau and a lady reporter. So we're just going to have a little chat out here on the porch."

I was surprised to hear Palmer so boldly identifying the relationship between Louisa May and me. Was it that obvious, or was this stout old man especially observant? I was also surprised that he didn't invite us inside after our long journey. Did we seem threatening?

After we'd settled on the porch with more small talk, the black woman came back. Though limping on a lame foot, she adeptly carried a tray of refreshments.

"Oh, honestly!" Mr. Palmer grunted. "Will you stop fussin' over us, Ruth? Thank you. But go on with you! We don't need nothin' else." Mr. Palmer's hand strayed to his trouser pocket, as it had once or twice before. It occurred to me that his old friend the jackknife was in there.

When Ruth opened the door again to depart, I heard a trace of voices on the other side. Adopting the most innocent and respectful face I had in my repertoire, I helped myself to apple cider and some rosemary biscuits.

"Now tell me, little Loulou," Mr. Palmer ventured. "What brings you and your friends to my humble farm?"

Though Margaret was sitting on the edge of her chair, bursting with a million questions, she wisely allowed Louisa May to take the lead.

"Well, sir." Louisa May carefully laid her biscuit on her napkin. "We heard that Ellery Channing was coming here, and we'd like to speak to him."

"I see." Mr. Palmer took a big bite of his biscuit and chewed thoughtfully for a minute. "It seems to me that a good man might like to travel from time to time for his own good reasons. Normally we would wait until such a man came home to speak to him. So I can't help wondering: Why would the three of you go to such trouble to try to chase him down?"

"He's my sister's husband," Margaret blurted out.

Mr. Palmer nodded, waiting for more as he shook biscuit crumbs from his beard.

"We're concerned about him," Louisa May supplied.

Mr. Palmer put on his 'Why would you be concerned about a grown man traveling?' face.

Louisa May reached in her pocket and handed over the poems that had led us there. We all munched dutifully on our biscuits while Palmer took his time to read them.

When he finished, Louisa May piped up again. "The unfinished poem is by Mr. Henry David Thoreau. We're actually worried about him, too. His cabin's been broken into, and he's gone missing. We feel he's gotten involved with something dangerous while living in his cabin in the woods. A woman was recently found killed out there. These poems suggest that Thoreau is angry at Ellery and that Ellery is worried for his life. We want to get to the bottom of it and make the woods safe again."

"So you've been investigating." Palmer rolled a crumb around in his mouth. "What's your theory?"

Here Louisa May looked to me for help, so I took my turn. "Well, three main possibilities have come to light," I said. "The first is that Thoreau is battling a vampire. We know that his family is infected with tuberculosis. The only member showing no infection is his sister Sophia, who wears a silver cross. She believes that her arrogant grandfather, who died of tuberculosis, has become a vampire and is feeding on the blood of family members. Perhaps Channing has come down with tuberculosis, and Thoreau is trying to convince him to take some kind of precaution against becoming a vampire."

Though Margaret was rolling her eyes, no one interrupted, so I continued. "The second possibility is that Thoreau is battling the Wendigo, an Indian monster that eats people. We know that Little Bear Polis gave Thoreau a dreamcatcher, which is used to catch nightmares. The Wendigo would be Thoreau's biggest nightmare because it represents the spirit of greed. Thoreau went to the woods to live a simple life, thereby attacking greed. Little Bear is making him a bigger dreamcatcher for the woods, and she may be the woman who was killed."

I wished at that moment that I had my phone to call Maria and ask if Little Bear had returned from her grandmother's house.

"Third," I went on, "there's the possibility that Thoreau is suffering from lycanthropy, the affliction of turning into a werewolf. According to legend, this can be caused by being bitten by another werewolf. We found all sorts of giant canine prints in the area where the woman was killed, as well as in Thoreau's cabin. Emerson says Thoreau likes to sleep under the light of the moon. Margaret says the philosophers' camping trip is heading to Wolf Swamp Gate. Maybe Thoreau is luring them there to feed the wolves, his endangered brethren."

It felt absurd offering these three fantastical theories. On the other hand, there is nothing absurd about the fantastical occurring in a dream. And I was now all too aware that this was a dream.

Palmer took me seriously. In fact, he looked disturbed, as though I'd put my finger on something that he was not at all happy about.

Margaret was getting impatient. "Come on, Palmer. Do you know anything that could help us?"

"Well," Mr. Palmer admitted, "as a matter of fact, I do."

CHAPTER
THIRTY-FIVE

The three of us stopped breathing, poised on pins and needles to hear what Mr. Palmer would say. He reached into the breast pocket of his jacket for a folded piece of paper.

"I am about to share something with the three of you," he announced. "I do so because you have entangled yourselves in something very big. It's bigger than Channing. It's bigger than he and Thoreau put together. It's bigger than the philosophers' camping trip."

Margaret was practically drooling.

"Now, Miss Margaret," Mr. Palmer continued, "with you being a reporter, it would not be fair or realistic for me to ask you to keep this thing a secret. Nevertheless, this thing needs to remain a secret. As it happens, I have read your book *Woman in the Nineteenth Century*, and I therefore have good reason to believe that you are a person with a strong conscience. So this is my deal for you: While *I* will not ask you to keep the secret, I believe that *your conscience* will. If it does, you must promise me, before these two young witnesses, that you will obey your conscience and keep the secret."

Margaret balked, as though suspecting that Palmer's deal was some kind of trick. But then her crocodile grin overtook her face, and she accepted the deal. "I promise."

Mr. Palmer nodded solemnly and handed over his paper. We unfolded it and read.

> Surely, surely, thou wilt trust me
> When I say thou dost disgust me.
> O, I hate thee with a hate
> That would fain annihilate;
> Yet sometimes against my will,
> Ellery, I love thee still.
> If thou won't support thy wife,
> Other duty claims thy life:
> Traitors must be stopped for good.
> Wilt thou help? Thou truly should.
> Meet me at the Wolf Swamp Gate
> Tuesday night at half past eight.
> — H.D. Thoreau

"It really is to Ellery!" Louisa May exclaimed.

Mr. Palmer flexed his eyebrows. "Ellery arrived here Sunday noon with this poem, which he had received the day before. He left for Wolf Swamp Gate about an hour ago."

"But who are the traitors?" I demanded. "Is Thoreau planning to sabotage the philosophers' camping trip? Why? Wasn't he invited?"

Mr. Palmer folded his arms across his chest and sank back in his rocking chair, apparently disinclined to say any more.

"It's almost seven already!" Margaret sprang from her chair, knocking her crumpled napkin to the floor. "Louisa May, where is this gate, and how long will it take us to get there?"

"Well, it's not really a gate," Louisa May explained. "It's a natural bridge across the Nashua River—a giant, fallen tree. I guess they call it a gate because it's the only bridge on the Nashua—the only way into the swamp from the west. When the water is high, it actually blocks boats."

"What are we waiting for?!" Margaret was already halfway down the porch steps. She looked back at us, knowing that she would never find the tree-bridge without Louisa May's help.

I hesitated. The whole thing sounded too dangerous. We didn't really know what we were getting into.

Ever the brave one—or maybe the rash one—Louisa May took a deep breath and set off after Margaret. Palmer saluted them resolutely.

"Mr. Palmer, tell me," I implored. "Is it safe?"

"No, sir," he reported, like a soldier to his commander. "It most certainly is *not* safe. But some things in life are important enough to take a risk."

"Is one of our theories correct?" I pressed.

Mr. Palmer blew out a long stream of breath. "They are all correct, metaphorically speaking. They are all incorrect, literally speaking. The arrogance of the vampire, the greed of the Wendigo, the violence of the werewolf—these are the essence of what you will see. But the monster itself is of a different kind altogether."

"Monster?"

Joseph Palmer began rocking in his rocking chair, lulling himself into a nap. I ran to catch up with Margaret and Louisa May.

"People never die in their dreams, right?"

That's the question I threw out to Louisa May and Margaret as we waded through the tall grass of Fruitlands' yard toward Wolf Swamp. I once read that if you die in your dream, you die in real life. But I didn't really believe it.

"Do you feel like you're dreaming, Llew?" Louisa May asked. "This *is* an awfully strange adventure."

Margaret plowed ahead with bright-eyed determination. "Only the dreamer shall understand realities, though in truth our dreaming must not be out of proportion to our waking."

"I think you wrote that somewhere once," Louisa May mused.

"Yes," Margaret concurred. "I think I did."

"I think it's true," I murmured, almost to myself. I was learning so much in the nineteenth century as Llew Willis— more than TJ could ever learn in a lifetime. Come to think of it, I wasn't sure I even *liked* TJ much anymore. He seemed shallow and self-absorbed. His big goal in life was to blow up an old boathouse. Why? To lash out, vaguely, blindly. Against what? Society?

No wonder he was miserable. His life goal was self-defeating. By fighting against society, TJ reified it, making it real, giving it too much credit. What the Transcendentalists showed is that, in the grand scheme of things, society is so inconsequential that it may as well not exist. Society is nothing but a speck on the toenail of nature. Nothing important or good has ever been accomplished by society. Everything important and good has been accomplished by individual genius that operates either oblivious to or in spite of society.

But if my dream was not out of proportion to my waking, then maybe there was hope for TJ yet. Maybe there was enough of Llew in him to become a philosopher.

We plodded along in silence for almost an hour. The landscape slowly turned from field to woods to swamp. The air was damp and heavy. Trees hung with moss. Our shoes and lower legs became covered in mud. Without much of a path, we wove between impassibly tangled scrub brush and random rock formations. We had to jump over sprawling puddles, which grew larger and larger into wetland. Dusk was setting in.

"Okay," Louisa May breathed at last, "if I remember right, Wolf Swamp Gate should be right around this bend."

We slunk around the bend. When I looked up after scrambling over a log, I almost cried out. There, at the top of the next rise, was the philosophers' campsite. It looked the same as in the painting—the painting that had started this whole thing. The memory of it was crystal clear in my mind.

I felt as though I was watching actors take the stage for a play I'd seen before. Everyone was getting into position.

https://concordlibrary.org/special-collections/emerson-celebration/Em_Con_80

Who are these men,
and what are they looking at?

CHAPTER
THIRTY-SIX

Louisa May, not being Ivy anymore, showed no recognition of the scene. She and Margaret crouched by me behind a jumble of rocks so we could see without being seen. Margaret pulled a pair of binoculars out of her satchel.

"That's them all right," she whispered. "I see Emerson in the middle by the tree and Agassiz at the stump on the left. One, two, three, four, five, six, seven, eight, nine, ten, eleven, twelve.... Wait a minute. There are thirteen of them. Who's the extra man?

"I think that's Joe Polis in the blue shirt with the rifle," Louisa May whispered. "He seems to be showing some of the others how to shoot."

For a moment, all I could focus on was the wise old tree in the middle of the scene. It stood shimmering, magnificently indifferent to the men beneath it. It made me think of something I'd heard Emerson say over dinner at the Saturday symposium: "The world is made of thickened light."

Though the statement had struck me as absurd when I'd first heard it, it now struck me as the secret that all great artists know. It was the secret that enabled William James Stillman to paint the philosophers' camping trip so compellingly. He had learned to see the true nature of nature.

My eye was drawn away from the tree by someone emerging from the tent.

"There's a fourteenth man coming out of the tent," I whispered. "I recognize him. He was at the Saturday symposium—the one who came late with the news that Thoreau had been arrested."

"Yes," Margaret whispered. "Smith. I believe he said his name was Daniel Duncan Smith, from Red River, Louisiana."

"But he's originally from that big pro-slavery family in Still River," Louisa May added.

"Where's Channing?" I asked.

"And where's Thoreau?" Margaret echoed.

"You see the direction Joe is shooting?" Louisa May asked. "That's the direction of the river."

"Most of them seem to be looking in that direction," I pointed out. I realized, however, that Margaret and Louisa May wouldn't care so much about seeing what the men were looking at, since they didn't know about the painting.

"They seem to be taking turns at target practice," Margaret observed. "I bet they set up a target on the other side of the river. That's what they're looking at."

Yes, that's what they're looking at now. But it's not half past eight yet.

I stood slowly, looking in the direction of the gate, realizing that we would never be able to see it from where we were. We had to get closer to the river. "Let's move down the slope a bit to see if we can spot Channing and Thoreau," I suggested.

Margaret stood slowly. "Agreed."

We began to creep to the right, through thick undergrowth, toward the river. Louisa May was behind us. All of a sudden I heard an "Ooof!" When I turned to look, she was face-down on the ground.

"What the devil?" Margaret exclaimed.

We bent to turn Louisa May over. I held her head and shoulders in my arms. "Louisa May," I rasped, "are you all right?"

"Mmmmmm," she moaned, her head lolling to the side.

She was breathing fine. I patted her cheeks. Her eyes fluttered open. She looked from me to Margaret and back again, confused.

"Are you all right?" I repeated.

"Mmm, yes," she replied, looking around. "I must have tripped and hit my head. I'm fine." She propped herself up on her elbow for a moment, getting her bearings. I helped her up.

As soon as she stood, she caught sight of the philosophers' camp. "Oh!" Her hand flew up to cover her mouth.

"What is it?" Margaret demanded. "What's the matter?"

Louisa May looked at me, eyes wide. "It's...."

"Yes!" I exclaimed. "It is!"

Ivy was back!

How could I tell? I could tell by the look on Louisa May's face when she caught sight of the philosophers' camp. There was no mistaking it: it was the look of recognition. When she turned to me with triumph in her eyes, I could almost see Ivy peering out. I'd never felt so happy to see someone in my whole life. I hugged Louisa May tightly.

Margaret glared at us, trying to figure out what was going on. If she caught any sign of an anachronism, it could get us booted out of the dream. We needed to get Ivy firmly into her role as quickly as possible.

I started leading Louisa May by the hand. "I thought if we moved down the slope, we might be able to spot Thoreau and Channing at the gate."

"Right!" Louisa May enthused.

Margaret scowled but followed along without further comment.

Fighting burs on our clothes, branches in our faces, and insects buzzing around our ears, we inched down the slope. Before long, we reached a ledge that dropped sharply down to the Nashua River, a still and deep-looking waterway.

We gathered along the edge, three in a row, to survey the riverbed. About 200 feet south, we could see Wolf Swamp Gate—a giant tree extending across the river where it became narrow between a craggy outcropping on either side. The tree lay several feet above the water. It had fallen from the other side, its roots still mostly grounded. Another fallen tree, half in the water, helped anchor it on our side.

From our new vantage point, we could barely see the philosophers' camp. Only the upper bodies of the men taking shooting lessons from Joe Polis appeared over the top of the rise. The rise became the craggy outcropping that anchored the bridge. The philosophers were almost directly above the bridge.

My heart started beating hard. I scanned the wooded shadows on the other side of the river, looking for signs of a monster. What would it be? Would the philosophers shoot at it?

CHAPTER
THIRTY - SEVEN

Margaret scanned the bridge with her binoculars. "There they are!"

Louisa May and I squinted at Wolf Swamp Gate. Soon, movement gave Thoreau and Channing away. They were climbing onto the bridge from our side. Each had a canvas bag and a coiled rope slung across his shoulder. They crawled across the giant tree trunk on their hands and knees. Before reaching halfway, Channing stopped. Thoreau continued on, stopping two thirds of the way to the other side.

If the philosophers were to look down from their camp, they would be able to see the bridge. The many trees on the craggy slope might obscure their view of Channing, but not of Thoreau. Still, the philosophers were not likely to notice him. The target that Joe Polis had set up for his shooting lesson was on a ledge on the other side of the river, farther south, directing everyone's attention away from the bridge. Had Thoreau arranged in advance for Joe to function as a double-agent among the campers?

Once in position, Thoreau and Channing took the trappings off their shoulders and started doing something.

"Can you see what they're doing?" I asked Margaret.

"They appear to be nailing their bags to the tree," she reported from behind her binoculars.

Once she said it, I discerned the swinging motion of the men's arms, and I could even hear some hammering, though it was much softer than the sound of the rifles going off.

Thoreau and Channing were nailing their bags to the south side of the tree so that the bags would be tacked to it tightly where we couldn't see them. When they were satisfied that the bags were secure, they began nailing their ropes to the same side of the tree, in a loop, so that both ends of the rope were fastened to the trunk at the same point. When these operations were complete, each man lowered himself into the loop of his rope and perched like a woodpecker on the side of the tree near his bag.

What in the world were they up to? What was inside those bags?

Being on the north side of the tree, we could no longer see Thoreau and Channing, except for a head occasionally popping up to look around. They were apparently waiting there with their mystery bags, their legs dangling over the river as if ready to drop into the water at any moment.

Time ticked excruciatingly by. Margaret and Louisa May and I sat motionless, waiting. Finally, the shooting lesson crescendoed to a noisy conclusion. Smoke from the rifles rose to the sky. Then the camp was quiet. I felt my stomach drop. It must be time.

Suddenly, a loud barking sound echoed across the riverbed. I nearly jumped out of my skin.

"That's just a night heron," Margaret informed us. "The call of the night heron sounds like a dog."

"Oh!" Louisa May exclaimed. "My homework assignment from Mr. Thoreau was to learn the call of the night heron."

"Well, then, congratulations." Margaret spoke distractedly. "Assignment fulfilled."

I noticed that Margaret's brow was beaded with sweat. She was more nervous than she was letting on.

Then we heard the barking sound again. It was growing louder.

"That's not a bird," I countered. "That really is a dog."

The word *dog* was barely out of my mouth before we saw motion on the opposite bank, north of the bridge. Something was barreling full speed out of the woods. It was too big for a bird. It was too big for a dog.

The three of us lunged forward, jaws dropping, eyes wide. And then, in the blink of an eye, the full scene unfolded before us in all its horror.

It was human beings—a man and a woman with the darkest shade of skin. The woman wore a crimson dress and headscarf. She held a tightly swaddled infant in her arms. The man's clothes were in tatters. He held a makeshift club in one hand and a dagger in the other.

The family hurtled down the wooded slope into the marshy bank of the river. They looked around in wild desperation, spotted the Wolf Swamp Gate, and started wading frantically toward it.

Just then a large brown dog burst through the thick curtain of vegetation. It was sleek and muscular, with crooked black eyes. Snarling with rabid hatred, the dog leapt into the water and bounded toward the fleeing family.

They would never make it. The dog was out of control, crazed with evil, going for the kill.

The man stopped and turned, club raised in one hand, dagger drawn in the other, ready to make his last stand. He pushed the woman and her baby toward the bridge. The woman clung to the man and cried out. It was the most heart-rending wail the Earth has ever heard.

The dog closed in. The man shouted. The woman ran. The dog pounced. The man lashed out. The dog yowled and fell back. The dagger dripped bright red with blood. The man turned to run. The dog rose from the water and launched itself at the man's back. A shot rang out. The dog halted in mid-air, fell with a splash, and lay still.

My head swung around to see the source of the deadly bullet. Drawn by the commotion, the philosophers had gathered in a line at the edge of their camp. Some were holding their rifles, some were aiming, but only Joe Polis's gun was smoking. Ring was standing next to him.

This is the painting that Ring later produced, under his real name, of what we all saw that night:

Slave Hunt, Thomas Moran, 1862 (www.reddit.com/r/museum/comments/
4s6lie/thomas_moran_slave_hunt_dismal_swamp_virginia_1862/)

More barking. My head swung back to the river. Two more dogs burst through the green curtain. They were heeding the commands of their owner, who jogged down the slope behind them, followed by another man.

Margaret gasped. "Slave hunters!"

"The devil!" the first slave hunter bellowed when he reached the bank. "He killed my best dog!"

Meanwhile, the escaped slave family had reached the tree-bridge. The man was hoisting the woman up onto it. When the lead slave hunter saw this, he whistled for the waiting dogs to attack. The dogs flew like arrows from a tightly strung bow toward the bridge.

Louisa May cried out. Her hands flew to her mouth in terror. I could scarcely breathe.

"Come on, Joe!" I screamed in my head. "Shoot those dogs! Shoot those hunters!"

What would happen to a Native American man who shot two white men in the nineteenth century? I wondered. *What would happen to him even if he only shot their vicious dogs?*

I didn't have time to come up with any answers. What happened next went down so fast that it was hard to make sense of it all.

As the escaped slave family raced across the bridge, Thoreau and Channing waved them to the other side.

Meanwhile, the lead slave hunter caught up with the dogs, who were slowed by the awkward climb onto the bridge. They whined and hesitated, afraid of crossing a tree so high above the river.

"Come on, you stupid mutts!" the slave hunter spat, hitting the nearest dog with the butt of his rifle.

At that moment, Thoreau and Channing dropped soundlessly from the bridge into the river.

As the escaped slave family clambered off the bridge on the other side, the two dogs and their master reached the middle of the bridge, moving slowly, single file, suspicious of the smoke now visibly rising from the two points on the bridge recently vacated by Thoreau and Channing. One dog ran ahead to give Channing's nest a sniff.

That's when the bridge exploded—first the double-flash, then the double-boom, then splinters flying everywhere, then a billowing black cloud.

I think I was momentarily blinded and deafened. Louisa May, Margaret, and I hit the dirt, cowering together in one big pile. Afterward, everything was completely, gloriously still again.

All I could think about as I slowly regained my senses was how much time and energy Thoreau's pencil graphite grinder must have saved him when he was making those bombs and how finely ground his black powder must have been.

CHAPTER
THIRTY-EIGHT

The escaped slave family survived the blast. We could see them scrambling up the wooded slope toward the philosophers' camp. Joe Polis was hurrying down to meet them. The rest of the campers, not having been prepared for what had happened, stood frozen to the ground.

Thoreau and Channing survived as well. We could see their heads bobbing downstream in the river. They were trying to swim toward our shore.

None of the dogs survived.

Only one of the slave hunters survived—the second one, who hadn't quite made it to the bridge. The blast had thrown him backward into the marshy bank.

As I watched, the slave hunter rose from the muck, choking and sputtering. Bewildered, he gazed at the bridge, which was no longer there. Two beats later, he registered the tree and body fragments scattered around. Two beats after that, he caught sight of Thoreau and Channing wading out of the river. Even from a distance, I could see a murderous rage spread across his face.

Louisa May and Margaret were focused on Thoreau, who faltered in the marshy bank and was momentarily pulled back into the current. They stood to run to him. But I could see the slave hunter hoisting his rifle to take aim at Channing, who was already pulling himself out of the water and up onto a boulder.

I stood. "CHANNING, GET DOWN!" I screamed at the top of my lungs.

A second later, a shot rang out. It came from the slave hunter's rifle. It ricocheted off the boulder where Channing had been seconds earlier, before he dove to the other side.

The slave hunter shook his head. Unable get a lock on me or the women, who had hit the dirt, he swung his rifle toward Thoreau, who was still struggling in the river. When Thoreau heard the shot at Channing, he dove under water for cover, but he was already back up for air.

Another shot rang out, this time from the philosophers' camp. The slave hunter tumbled awkwardly forward and lay still. When I turned to look where the shot had come from, I saw Emerson's gun smoking.

Ivy and I didn't stay after that. This time it was my fault. But maybe I did it on purpose. All I said was: "Margaret, I'm quite sure that neither you nor anyone else ever reported this story."

Suddenly, I was back in my modern bed, in my modern room, in Red River, Louisiana, waking up from a long, hard dream.

According to the historical record, the philosophers made it to the Adirondacks and camped for a month at Follensbee

Pond, not far from the Canadian border and the farm refuge that radical abolitionist John Brown had set up for freed slaves. Had the philosophers taken a family of escaped slaves with them? Even if they had, such information would be forever missing from the historical record.

I threw on some clothes and trotted out of the house. It was early in the morning—almost dawn. As I approached Ivy's house, I could see light in one of the rooms. I called Ivy's name a few times. The window popped open. It was her.

"Come on!" I whispered. "I know where the painting is!"

Ivy climbed out the window, and we headed for the cabin. Still reeling from the drama of the dream, we chattered about it all the way there.

"That was cool," Ivy remarked, "how you saved Channing."

"Well," I demurred, "I couldn't have done it if you hadn't gotten us to the river in time. Do you think anything like that take-down at Wolf Swamp really happened?" I asked.

"No," Ivy conceded. "But it *could* have."

"Do you think Joseph Palmer was hiding escaped slaves?" I pressed. "I mean, in the dream and for real?"

"Absolutely," Ivy pronounced. "And he wasn't the only one—for real. There was a whole Underground Railroad—a network of abolitionists throughout the country who would hide the escaped slaves on their way north. They had a newspaper called *The North Star*."

"But do you think it's really true that there were slave hunters out trying to catch escaped slaves?" I pressed.

Ivy nodded grimly. "In 1850 they passed a law requiring everyone—North or South—to return escaped slaves to their masters. It was illegal to help slaves escape. By then all the Transcendentalists were in on the Underground Railroad, including the Alcott family, the Thoreau family, and Emerson, who publicly denounced the law. They called it the 'Bloodhound Law' because of the dogs."

"Those dogs would have killed that family."

"Sometimes slave hunters hunted for bounty, sometimes just for sport."

That information was so deeply chilling to me that I needed to change the subject.

After I reminded Ivy about the rolling pin I had retrieved from Maria's garret, she immediately knew where the painting was stashed.

It was a little creepy venturing into the woods when it was still so dark out, but both of us knew the way well. When we arrived, the cabin seemed still as a tomb—exactly the same as we'd left it. I thought about the two sets of Civil War uniforms in the trunk in the cellar. What was the story behind them and the man who had built the cabin? Why build such an exact replica of Thoreau's cabin?

On entering the cabin this time, I couldn't believe I had never noticed the trapdoor in the ceiling. Still, the door had no handle that might have called attention to it. Standing on a chair, I was able to push the door open. It was a garret all right. Not just one but two paintings nestled amid its cobwebs. Both were bare canvasses, rolled up and fastened in waterproof bags.

I carefully unrolled the first painting onto the bed. It was *Slave Hunt*, by Thomas Moran (a.k.a. Ring). Ivy and I gazed at it in the dawn that was now penetrating the cabin window. We were blown away by its terrible beauty. I could only bear to look at it because I had seen for myself—though only in a dream—that the family had escaped. Ivy ended up donating that painting to the Philbrook Museum of Art in Tulsa, Oklahoma, where the public can view it.

Rolled up with the painting was a letter in an opened envelope that had been sent from Philadelphia.

To: Mr. Daniel Duncan Smith
    Red River Plantation
    Louisiana, USA

June 15, 1862

My good sir,

In the attached package you will find the work you commissioned: an oil painting on canvas of the memory-ravaging incident at the philosophers' camp.

You asked me to send it as a gift to the honorable Mr. Henry David Thoreau in Concord, Massachusetts. I have just learned, however, of his tragic death from tuberculosis. I am therefore sending it to you instead.

Thank you for your payment. It will help launch a career in which I hope to explore, question, and celebrate man's place in nature.

Yours truly,
Thomas Moran (Ring)

Also with this painting was another letter, this one never sent.

To: Mr. Henry David Thoreau
    Texas Street
    Concord, Massachusetts

June 14, 1862

My dear Henry David,

I've just received word from friends of your sister that your long struggle with tuberculosis has taken a turn for the worse. For years now, I've wanted to tell you what an inspiration you have been to me. Due to the discreet nature of our shared cause, I have refrained from writing. But now, with you in your darkest hour, it is necessary to take the risk.

When I returned home to Red River after the incident at Wolf Swamp Gate, I built a cabin for myself in the woods, modeled board-for-board on your cabin at Walden Pond. Here I entertain visitors who are prepared to set out on a journey toward the North Star. I like to think that you may have met some of them along the way.

I never quit the Unitarian Church, since being a reverend often gave me access to the information I needed to conduct my more discreet business.

When the war broke out, I joined the Confederate Army as a chaplain. As soon as I was well established, I joined the Union Army as well. This arrangement, though highly dangerous, is conducive to working toward freedom and justice for all.

I confess to you that I have betrayed my entire family, who continue to fight on the wrong side of this cause. My twin brother Darvin is dead, practically by my own hand, since it was I who betrayed his brigade to their enemy.

I assure you, Henry David, that you alone showed me the way to my true, though painful, calling in life. I think of myself as working right alongside you, shoulder to shoulder, even though we are separated by so many miles. We are, after all, connected by that invisible railroad track that is destined to save this country from its wickedness.

My best wishes to you and your family. I remain ever hopeful that, when we finally win this cursed war, I will again travel north to embrace you and enjoy some time with you in the woods.

In the meantime, I've asked a talented young painter we both know to send you a gift. Please share it far and wide with anyone who may find the courage to join our cause in whatever way they can.

Yours truly,
Daniel Duncan Smith

So Ivy was descended from a Civil War spy. Somehow that did not surprise me.

Ivy's granddad (Daniel Duncan Smith III) had carefully saved the two sets of uniforms and all the papers testifying to his granddaddy's espionage in the Civil War. No wonder Mr. Smith had celebrated Memorial Day with such inexplicably secretive exuberance every year—he was so proud and so ashamed of his family, all at the same time.

The second painting was an unsettling surprise.

As it turned out, Louisa May Alcott's youngest sister, Abigail May Alcott, grew up to be an accomplished artist. Many years after the incident at Wolf Swamp Gate, when Abby May was a professional artist living in Paris, France, she painted a portrait called *La Negresse*.

The expression of forlorn dignity on this young woman's face brilliantly tells the whole story of slavery in one fell swoop. Considered the masterpiece of Abby May's career, *La Negresse* was exhibited at the Paris Salon, a rare honor for a female artist in the nineteenth century.

La Negresse, Abigail May Alcott, 1879
(https://commons.wikimedia.org/wiki/File:May_Alcott_Nieriker_-_La_Negresse_-_1879.jpg)

Given the orange headscarf of *La Negresse*, Ivy and I believe her to be Abby May's imagined portrait of the unidentified woman who was killed in the woods near Concord. Perhaps there were originally four members of the escaped slave family that Thoreau and Channing had saved. One member, perhaps the mother's sister, had arrived early as a scout. Joseph Palmer had sent her on to Thoreau's cabin at Walden Pond, the next stop on her family's Underground Railroad journey. She had made it, but not without attracting the attention of slave hunters. With Thoreau being locked in jail that night, no one had been present to help her escape the bloodhounds.

Ivy and I tucked the paintings carefully back in their wrappers, and back in their hiding place, where they would stay until she and her mother could decide what to do with them.

Ivy's granddad died later that same day. There would be no fireworks display on the neighborhood pond that year. My explosives would stay forever buried in the woods—unless someday I needed them in the line of duty.

Ivy and I met on the roof of the boathouse on Memorial Day to watch the sun go down. I brought a box of sparklers. Once it was dark enough, we lit them one by one, to remember all the victims of the Civil War.

I had just finished reading Thoreau's book, *Walden; or, Life in the Woods*, which Ivy had let me borrow from the drawer of the cabin. Since I had brought it along to return to her, and since it almost felt like Spiderland out there on the neighborhood pond with her, I decided to perform my favorite passage of the book out loud. The passage is from the end of the book, where Thoreau explains why he decided to leave his cabin after two years.

> I left the woods for as good a reason as I went there. Perhaps it seemed to me that I had several more lives to live, and could not spare any more time for that one. It is remarkable how easily and insensibly we fall into a particular route, and make a beaten track for ourselves. I had not lived there a week before my feet wore a path from my door to the pond-side; and though it is five or six years since I trod it, it is still quite distinct. It is true, I fear, that others may have fallen into it, and so helped to keep it open. The surface of the earth is soft and impressible by the feet of men; and so with

the paths which the mind travels. How worn and dusty, then, must be the highways of the world, how deep the ruts of tradition and conformity!...

I learned this, at least, by my experiment: that if one advances confidently in the direction of his dreams, and endeavors to live the life which he has imagined, he will meet with a success unexpected in common hours. He will put some things behind, will pass an invisible boundary; new, universal, and more liberal laws will begin to establish themselves around and within him; or the old laws be expanded, and interpreted in his favor in a more liberal sense, and he will live with the license of a higher order of beings. In proportion as he simplifies his life, the laws of the universe will appear less complex, and solitude will not be solitude, nor poverty poverty, nor weakness weakness. If you have built castles in the air, your work need not be lost; that is where they should be. Now put the foundations under them.

Ivy applauded enthusiastically. I handed Thoreau's book to her. She pulled something out of her pocket. It was the dreamcatcher bookmark. She tucked the bookmark back into the book, just as she'd found it. Then she threw the book into the pond, where it sank like a stone, without a trace.